NICOLAS JOLY, born in 1945, h
dynamics for over 25 years, and i
of France's foremost winemakers. Following his studies at
Columbia University, he joined JP Morgan in New York. He
was posted to London, but left in 1977 to run his family's
vineyard, Coulée de Serrant. Having worked with modern
agriculture and observed its negative effects on nature, he
came across a book on biodynamic farming and began
experimenting, fascinated by the ideas he found there. Later
he discovered that a movement existed around the founder of
biodynamics, Rudolf Steiner, and Joly connected with others.
He suffered much opposition until the end of the 1990s,
when the quality of his wines, with their unique and true
appellations, spoke for themselves. Nicholas Joly now teaches
around the world as one of the pioneers of biodynamic
viticulture.

WHAT IS BIODYNAMIC WINE?

THE QUALITY, THE TASTE, THE TERROIR

NICOLAS JOLY

CLAIRVIEW

Translated from French by Matthew Barton

Clairview Books
Hillside House, The Square
Forest Row, East Sussex
RH18 5ES

www.clairviewbooks.com

Published by Clairview 2007
Reprinted 2011

A catalogue record for this book is available from the British Library

ISBN 978 1905570 09 6

Cover by Andrew Morgan Design
Typeset by DP Photosetting, Neath, West Glamorgan
Printed and bound by Cromwell Press Limited, Trowbridge, Wiltshire

To my parents, my children and my wife.

Also to Xavier Florin and Maria Thun, who brought their vision and depth to biodynamics.

Contents

Passion for Wine and the Appellation d'Origine Contrôlée (AOC)

A passion for wine is spreading like wildfire through the world, like a quest for something to give life greater sense and joy. Wine-lovers compare the idiosyncratic tastes of grapes growing in different locations of the globe. With something bordering on apprehension they relish the brand and trade name implacably imposed on a grower despite an increasingly disrupted climate. They leave the bottle open to 're-taste' it the next day and the day after that. They deliberate, calculate, wonder, question and get carried away with their particular enthusiasms. This is indeed a growing passion which touches all professions and social classes, which sharpens each person's senses, impressions and emotions. Though some degree of knowledge develops from this passion, it never quite hardens into certainty. It remains, instead, something against which to continually test one's faculties and one's desire to apprehend the realities of another, fluctuating and intangible, world — that of aromas, tastes, balances and harmonies. A fragile world, for which those of an artistic sensibility always feel a certain nostalgia, which expresses itself subtly, discretely and almost shyly through matter. We desire to understand how an equilibrium sometimes so delicate is achieved; how these bright and dark moods, these sorrows and joys of the vine can ultimately become tastes, scents or harmonies of an almost musical nature.

Basically all this underlies, and justifies, the profound concept of the 'appellations contrôlées' or 'regulated wine of origin'.* Back in the 1930s when France, followed swiftly by many other countries, created the AOC standards, what was its aim? It simply wished to protect a sum of knowledge, an accumulation of experience, a finger-tip feeling several centuries old that had led people to plant wine in certain 'good' locations. What did a 'good location' mean in that less abstract era? Quite simply a place where 'Lady Vine' felt at ease, could give full 'voice' to her happiness and sing forth without hindrance. We will find that this song is not always as joyous as we think. For the moment it is enough to understand that, when a vine is situated where it can unfold its full potency as a highly atypical and self-willed vegetative being, it will imbue its fruit with a taste endowed by the place in which it grows. Simple enough? It weds the soil via its roots, uniting with it intimately, and receiving through its leaves all the climatic conditions specific to that area. These

---

* 'Appellation Contrôlée' is a guarantee that a wine has been produced in a specific location (appellation), by a particular method, with approved grape varieties and in controlled quantities. The system is legally defined and regulated in France.

are composed of the different qualities of heat which arise at different moments, of variations of light intensity, of winds full of gentleness or revolt, of modest or abundant rains, of morning mists or brief twilights: all these aspects of weather combine to become first vegetative matter and ultimately fruit. But how does this actually happen?

Take a look at a field of vines, in spring first of all, then in the autumn: you have to realize that all these branches, these leaves, and several tonnes of grapes per hectare – which were mere buds 6 months before – are barely composed of the substance of the soil, as people too often assume. On the contrary, the major part of their substance comes from photosynthesis, a wretched word shorn of beauty which does not come close to expressing a still unexplained mystery that the scientific world observes without being able to reproduce. Photosynthesis refers to the conversion of heat, light and air – a world, therefore, of almost intangible forces like the tastes and aromas we mentioned above – into real matter composed of carbohydrate, starch, sugars etc. If one excludes water from these substances – thus remaining with 'dry matter' as science terms it – over 92 percent derives from photosynthesis, and thus only a very small amount can be attributed to the soil itself. From spring to autumn, too often without realizing it, we witness the plant world 'materializing' an almost invisible world, a process in which the agency of climate plays an important part. Into matter and substance descend subtleties of taste, colour and scent so prized by wine-lovers: truffle, olive oil, coffee, cigar, tea etc. Each plant accomplishes this task in its 'own' manner, with its unique nuances which give us such pleasure if we know how to recognize them, and can distinguish them from the artificial flavours that technology secretly infiltrates into our food and drink.

With something akin to hypersensitivity the vine excels in its capacity to create nuances of taste. It is therefore interesting to try to understand in detail the deep nature of our friend the vine or, let us say, to enter into its secret gestures so as to approach the very nature of wine.

What place does the vine occupy in the plant kingdom? What is its character, its conduct, its unique nature? Like all living beings, none of whom are merely driven by blind cause and effect, this question takes us in an important direction. To answer it we need to return to the botanists of the Middle Ages and their rich store of knowledge, so little understood by our modern era. They had a very different view of plants from us. Matter itself, which we are so interested in nowadays, right down to its tiniest atoms, was for them merely something that served to fill a form, like the dough in a bread tin. What medieval scholars were interested in was the mould or form itself, in other words the various forces which 'sculpt' the vegetable world differently in each instance, and which give it a particular aspect and mode of behaviour. This was nothing to do with genes – which of course they had never heard of. But if one had talked to them about genes they would probably have replied: 'Why concern yourself with the obedient labourers who merely carry out orders? Instead study the architects who arrange and organize these genes.' Thus they would direct us to the whole system of energies which physicists are just beginning to comprehend today through magnetic resonance imaging, something which bio-dynamics makes full use of. Reading Hildegard von Bingen,* Culpeper† and many other famous authors of this period, an era so poorly understood by modern science, we find that all of them approach the plant world through what Plato calls the 'four states of matter' (see Plate 1). Thanks to this formidable body of knowledge one can develop a quite different perspective on the vine and wine.

This ancient wisdom can be briefly and simply, though very imperfectly, summed up as follows. The earth is subject to a force – gravity – that holds sway over every living being and thus also ourselves. It is gravity, this omnipresent force, which makes a stone fall when we throw it, which makes rain fall to earth, and which leaves us feeling so heavy after a day spent working hard. It is by virtue of this force that atoms coalesce, that matter forms and can attain a state of solidity. Without it the physical world, the earth's physical substance, would not exist.

---

* Blessed Hildegard of Bingen (1098–1179), a German teacher, monastic leader, mystic, author, and composer of music.
† Nicholas Culpeper (1616–1654), an English botanist, herbalist, physician, and astrologer.

Most fortunately, though, this force is counterbalanced by another, an opposite polarity. In the West we refer to this as 'solar attraction', and in the East it is often described as the force of levitation. Acting in opposition to gravity this leads towards a state of weightlessness. In physical terms heat embodies this force most clearly, which is thus one of rising or lifting from the earth. Just observe how every flame emits an ascending shimmer of heat. Heat dispels and disperses matter. Heated up, a heavy piece of metal turns to liquid, and then soon enters a gaseous state, delivered of its weight. This reveals the impermanence of matter and the physical world, which oscillates between the visible and the invisible – a theme we will return to later. The human being is also subject to this force, and it is this which indirectly – a subject in itself – enables him to wake up in the morning feeling light and renewed. It is this, likewise, which lends us wings to soar above the day's vicissitudes when we hear a piece of good news, and which plays such an important part in feelings of enthusiasm.

The great sages of the past stated that there were two intermediary states between these two forces. Descending from above, from a more rarefied condition, the first of these is air and light. This is the first condition with a slightly ter-restrial or physical quality. Air and light are closely con-nected, the latter becoming visible to us by means of the former. Without air the sky would not appear blue to us. Passing beyond the layers of atmosphere we find the sky is dark, opaque. The air has little weight but it is still, nevertheless, subject to gravity, a fact which, fortunately for us, keeps it closely wrapped around and enfolding the globe. When compressed (excessive gravity) the air actually grows more dense. These examples allow us to grasp the true nature of air and light as a first state of matter subject to density.

Next comes the liquid state. This condition, whose archetype is water, can be seen as occupying an intermediary position between the solar, ascending laws, and those of the earth. Water is more subject to gravity than air, and thus heavier and more earthly in nature. It is poised midway between the earth's gravitational attraction and the rising solar forces. It grows hard as a stone in cold conditions, clearly subject to gravity in a mineral-like fashion. Heat, on the other hand, releases it from earthly laws, enabling it to escape upwards as mist and fog. Archimedes tells us that water relieves us of some of our weight. Some of the pleasure of swimming is in being partly cushioned from the tug of gravity. We ourselves are composed of more than 90 percent water, which also helps explain the effect of various water treatments and therapies. In all this the important thing to note is that air and liquid are intermediary states in a progressive descent towards our earth's solid mineral substance. No life is possible on earth without passing initially through a liquid state — and the same applies of course to plants.

But why this long preamble in a book about wine? Well, so as to develop some understanding of the way in which plants relate to these four terrestrial conditions, and thus discover the profoundly atypical nature of the vine.

One can say, in general, that each plant reveals its relationship to earthly forces of gravity in its roots, to the watery state in its leaves, to the light in its capacity to bloom, and to warmth and heat in its power to fruit (see diagram below). It should be added that these four aspects also interpenetrate each other in the plant.

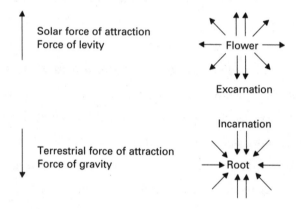

Solar force of attraction
Force of levity

Flower

Excarnation

Incarnation

Terrestrial force of attraction
Force of gravity

Root

All this could be described in length and detail, and should be understood in very specific, tangible terms. But where it becomes still more interesting is in the discovery that certain plants establish such relationships with *extreme originality*. Let's take a few simple examples to start with: a plant whose archetypal nature is to develop a strong affinity with the light will absorb it better, and can express or manifest this particular quality in a ravishing blossom. The lily is an example of this, a flower that adorned the flag of the French royalty. If the lily did not have this strong connection with light its power to bloom would be considerably less.

A different plant, closely connected with water such as rhubarb, will be able to produce big and abundant leaves. One intimately related to warmth and heat will receive from it a powerful fruit or seed-forming force. We can see this in grains and cereals where each grain sown multiplies a hundredfold.

All this becomes more complex when mother nature departs from her habitual schemas and plays with these four states of matter with such ingenuity and inventiveness that the result is sometimes very difficult to decipher. One example is the carrot which uses its floral capacity to colour and perfume its root, thus rendering the flower itself a poor and unattractive specimen. The pine tree pours its strong connection with the forces of warmth not into fruit but into its inflammable resin, thus endowing itself with the capacity to resist a greater degree of cold than most other plants. The willow is strongly con-nected not just to water but also to light. Because of this it does not form big leaves but manages to exhale this water through its leaves, and to evaporate it at the same time as attaining a honeyed state in its delicate flowers, of which the bees are so fond. It can also colour its wood a vivid yellow. The nettle (see Plate 2) does not put its connection with warmth into its seeds but into its leaves. Used as an infusion sprayed on vines, this gives them the capacity to maintain their sap circulation even at times of drought. Citronella takes the strength of taste destined for the fruit it does not form and puts it into its leaves.

In the cinnamon, taste descends right into the bark! The toughness of wood can ascend somewhat into the leaf of the magnolia ... And so on, and so forth.

Thus there is a secret language sometimes very subtle and difficult to decode. We can admire the ancient scholars who first deciphered this script and then linked it on occasion to very specific planetary or stellar forces whose effect they identified in matter. They also used this knowledge in very precise ways to create powerful remedies. This ability to observe life directly can still be found amongst peoples said to be 'primitive', who know of remarkable properties in the vegetable and animal world that surrounds them. The ancients did not have the same type of intelligence as we understand the word today, nor sophisticated instruments which our modern researchers depend on for their narrowly focused and strictly physical understanding of the world. They had other faculties instead which enabled them to tap into the deep messages of their senses. One can see this in very simple things such as the way people of the past knew how to cut a plant or tree at the right moment, in accordance with its native characteristics, or, let us say, its originating force. This optimized its effects somewhat like a musical note which uses its surroundings to resonate effectively. In olden times, for example, without any calendar of planetary move-ments, people knew an oak tree should be felled when Mars was in the descendant.

Each plant is an enigma to be solved, a labyrinth of complexity we need to approach with care. Goethe drew our attention to this in his book on plants, speaking of a kind of primordial or archetypal plant whose template, as it were, could be rediscovered amongst the innumerable differences of form and behaviour that plants develop in response to earthly conditions and diversity. Rediscovering this secret language leads us to a different understanding of medicinal plants and those used to make biodynamic preparations. Biodynamic agriculture is spreading fast in the realm of viti-culture because – when properly applied, and when the plants cultivated by this means are fully understood – it has powerful effects on the quality and taste of wine.

Medicinal plants, including the vine, are ones which heal due to their very diverse, atypical characteristics. Sometimes such a plant will activate in its roots, stalk, flowers or fruit one or several processes 'normally' situated elsewhere. The beetroot, for instance, directs the abundant sugars synthe-sized by its leaves not into fruit but into its root! The maple directs these sugars into its sap or syrup. A medicinal plant heals, ultimately, by virtue of being atypical. And to under-stand why these medicinal plants heal we need to under-stand that human beings also contain these four states of matter. We can rediscover them in our four temperaments,*

---

* An ancient doctrine applied to medicine by Hippocrates (c. 460–c. 370 BC). The temperaments – choleric, sanguine, melancholic, phlegmatic – refer to distinct personality types. See further in Gilbert Childs, *Understand Your Temperament!* (Sophia Books, 1995).

of which one is always predominant. No one will dispute that choleric people, through their stronger connection with heat, often seem to be on the brink of exploding (though they actually explode less frequently than one might think!). The sanguine person, always in movement, is as though borne on breezes and wafts of air. The phlegmatic benefits from his particular relationship to water and fluid through the inertia which enables him to navigate life's obstacles with good humour. Nothing suits him better than floating along contentedly in the swim of things! The melancholic rarely succeeds in overcoming the underlying note of sadness which his somewhat excessive connection with the earth, and the weight of matter, imposes on him. (Paradoxically, though, a good means of making him laugh is to tell him how sad life is!) All these things are elaborated by Hippocrates, who says that an illness often begins due to a disharmony between these four states in a specific part of the body. In trying to observe — ah, such a difficult thing, and something a microscope could never manage — where a process is out of balance, herbal medicine aims to offer a remedy by prescribing a plant or animal organ which innately embodies this specific connection or aspect. In this context a plant is no longer viewed as merely the bearer of substances or molecules, but as a gesture or potential link to the dynamic process it derives from its species. This is also how we can understand anthroposophic medicine*, which is still in its infancy, and, in a certain way, biodynamics too.

Let us take the example of the nettle to illustrate this in very brief outline, and to bring us a little closer to this whole approach. Though it may seem far-fetched, the nettle can help us, firstly, to better understand wine and its medicinal properties; and secondly to understand the vine and the choice of plants which help it accomplish its task in the face of an increasingly disrupted climate.

A quick glance at the nettle can show us that, like a sensitive and experienced diplomat, it seems to focus its activities more at its centre than its extremities: its roots remain close to the surface and decline to go very deep into the soil; its flowers which are spread the length of its stalk, rather than just emerging from the top, are both discrete and rather unattractive. As for its fruit it remains a minuscule, poorly developed, green grain. (See illustration over, also Plate 2.)

The nettle shows us, therefore, that it concentrates on its leaves: their transparent shimmer, almost floral in nature, and their burning sting, are qualities which ought not to be there in the normal run of things. We know that the leaf is the plant's mediating organ between its roots at one extremity and its fruits at the other. So it is easy to understand that the

---

* A holistic and salutogenetic approach to health that focuses on ensuring that the conditions for health are present in a person; combating illness is often necessary but is insufficient alone. The approach was founded in the 1920s by Rudolf Steiner (1861–1925).

nettle is a plant which directs towards its centre what many other plants express at their extremities. It is this fact of resembling something centred in its middle region, or, if you like, of balancing two extremes, which makes the nettle so beneficial for the human heart. This too is a central organ which continually tries to reconcile or balance what we load upon ourselves in our everyday lives, and mediate the often quite chaotic influx from our metabolic system on the one hand and our nervous system on the other. Rudolf Steiner* said of the nettle that it is an almost irreplaceable and indispensable plant. The vine receives it as infusion with particular gratitude at times of dryness or drought. It can also be used as a liquid manure, just to improve soils, as long as its smell is not too strong: the soil dislikes a stench.

This is a very brief glimpse of the immense knowledge of plants which people once possessed, which Goethe first, and then Rudolf Steiner, founder of biodynamic agriculture, took

---

* Austrian-born philosopher and scientist who developed 'anthroposophy', a system of knowledge that offers holistic and innovative approaches to education, agriculture, medicine, economics, the arts, and many other fields.

up again so ably and developed further. Ultimately we are interested not only in plants' physical aspects but in their whole mode of life and the energies and gestures that inform them. This botanical body of knowledge has now culminated in the wonderful books by Pelikan* and Grohman† which give us very tangible and living insight into the profound and healing reality of plants without referring merely to their molecules. One can see each plant as a melody, and their totality as an orchestral ensemble and continually changing consonance. It is this 'globality' which can heal more than each individual note of the harmony, of which our modern, scientific world is often all too ignorant through lack of knowledge. The younger generation, hopefully, will engage more fully with these new ways of perceiving, which can sustain us and bring to life our dry and abstract view of nature.

We have now learned a little more fluency in the language which allows us insight into the profound nature of our friend the vine. Of course, like every plant it is pulled in two directions: by gravity towards the centre of the earth, and by warmth and light towards the sun. The Greeks formulated this by saying that the vine is Dionysian in contrast to more Apollonian plants, and we can now grasp what they meant. An Apollonian type of plant is one which loves nothing better

---

* Wilhelm Pelikan, *Healing Plants* (Mercury Press, 1997).
† Herbert Grohmann, *The Plant* (SteinerBooks, 1996).

than to climb heavenwards with an uprightness that nothing can deflect, as if to rejoin the sun. Cypress trees, so fine and delicate, which climb to 10 or 20 metres, give us a perfect image of the Apollonian plant. (See Plate 3.)

The Christian religion chose wheat as the Apollonian plant par excellence. No one can really explain how a stalk as slender as that of wheat can climb so high and defy the wind. This is, indeed, only possible where a healthy agriculture allows silica to play its full role. Let me mention in passing that our modern types of wheat have, alas, degenerated due to the range of treatment they receive – including the dreadful height-limiting herbicides which stunt their growth to 60 centimetres. They are then no longer able to provide the human being with all the qualities which this plant originally embodied. It is now even accused of causing allergies, whereas in fact we ourselves have created them!

The opposite of the Apollonian type of plant is the Dionysian, which shows us a powerful predilection for earthly forces of gravity. Such a plant gathers in its roots a great strength for penetrating the hardest and poorest soils, and for making itself at home there! A stalk of wheat could never manage this. And yes, you have no doubt guessed it, the archetypal representative of the Dionysian plant is the vine (see Plate 5). In fact one cannot fully understand a vine without understanding its opposite. The forces which cypress or wheat direct into their branches or stems to defy gravity and elevate themselves ever higher and higher towards the sun, are directed in the vine to its roots, enabling it to delve ever deeper and penetrate even the most obdurate and stony soil. This strength also enables it to be quite thrifty in its need for nutrients. One can find vine roots sometimes as far as 30 or 40 metres away from the plant, or even more. Even if the soil is largely rocky the vine will take advantage of the slightest crack to insert its roots. This extreme connection with earthly forces means that the vine is almost incapable of accomplishing any heavenward ascent unaided. I do not say, however, that the vine resembles a liana — something often stated, but really quite inappropriate since the vine is much more than just this. As soon as its branches lift a little way above the soil, unless they have something to attach themselves to, they are recaptured by the forces of the earth. They therefore have to be propped and trellised, helped by means of wires or posts or dead trees — as people do in Portugal sometimes — to find the support which will allow them to climb upwards: something of which they actually have great need. When, towards the end of spring, one observes the almost desperate motions which the vine makes to hurl itself into the air, one could aptly call this a nostalgia for the sun. Each branch which falls is on the search for any aid, however slight, which will allow it to make yet another attempt to climb upwards again.

One has to understand that the vine is the earth's prisoner, imprisoned by the gravity which holds sway over it. This is described in the Greek myth in which Persephone, the daughter of Demeter, is kidnapped by Pluto – the sub-terranean god of the underworld who symbolizes gravity itself (and willpower). It is thus that Persephone becomes a prisoner of the harsh laws of the earth, like her son Dionysus who is subsequently torn to pieces by the Titans. They too symbolize the forces of the earth. Gravity is the force which imprisons what surfaces in the earthly domain, clothing itself in matter and isolating and thus separating itself from an overall context of energies. It individualizes in the physical realm, giving birth to the human being's sense of a separate self, of 'I', that little word which, for better or worse, distin-guishes us from each other. And this lost globality which we have to try to recover as human beings is, you can say, the second or reborn Dinoysus whose heart is redeemed and entrusted to Zeus.

The vine is thus the archetypal plant of the earth, which joins in deepest union with it, accepting all its forces of gravity. Just look at its flowers, almost concealed in its bosom and turned earthwards. Plants generally flower at the top, above the leaves. The vine is too drawn towards the earth to do this. To find the flowers almost hidden at its heart one has to move back its stems and leaves. But despite their smallness and discreteness we should not mis-judge them: they generate a perfume one can detect from several metres away, thus showing that they retain a strong connection to the solar realm even if the earth condition dominates. Being a prisoner of the earth does not mean we lose all links to the solar realm of generating forces. On the contrary, it is this isolation which gives rise to a *greater longing for the solar realm,* as though by reaction. *The vine draws its capacity to create a product as noble and complex as wine from the fact that it is so radically atypical.*

And this allows us to raise an important question never tackled by our schools of viticulture, which are generally too far removed, unfortunately, from such qualitative considerations. As winegrowers is it our task, perhaps, to help the vine escape the earth a little, that is to give it some means to emerge from its terrestrial 'prison'? Do we need to help raise it up and become somewhat more Apollonian, with fencing or pruning that enables it to climb; or perhaps just to do this more subtly by spraying a Cypress infusion on its leaves? Or should we rather accept or reinforce this connection with gravity by, for example, cutting it back down each year when pruning, in order to force it to remain close to the ground? This, in other words, would mean stimulating and reinforcing its predominating temperament which nature gave it to enable it to survive in such difficult conditions. Couldn't such an action give the wine still more verve or vitality? A comparable approach can be found in education: to what extent should we indulge or oppose a child to help him achieve the best intrinsic harmony? How far can one go? In the same way the viticulturist needs to consider the age of his vines, the generosity of the soil, the latitude of the location, the direction of the slopes, the prevailing winds, hydrometric considerations etc., before taking a decision which will imbue his grape harvest with abundance, resilience or atypicity – unless he resorts to deceitful technology! Weighing up all these aspects each viticulturist will choose his own path, drawing on his *own creative response,* so as to better harmonize his vines with their archetypal forces.

Shouldn't such things form an intrinsic part of agricultural courses? Should we not give students creativity and liberty by offering a much broader and profounder kind of knowledge than they will gain from fixed formulae or a mechanistic approach that is incapable of grasping the real nature of plants, and which instead focuses almost exclusively on economics and the market? In a location that is well-suited for winegrowing a wise agriculture allows the vines to fully unfold and express the profound life within them. Where a viticulturist can put his personal stamp on his vines through carefully chosen methods of cultivation, such creativity will certainly find its way into his wine. We will return to this theme in Chapter 5.

Only an agriculture that takes full account of the laws of nature and its underlying forces, so widely ignored nowadays, can help generate the authentic diversity of expression implicit in each AOC. To think that this work should be undertaken at the cellar is, as we will see, a lack of understanding generally subscribed to by winegrowers who have had to transform their cellars into factories in order to try –

imperfectly – to correct the agricultural errors of which they are hardly aware.

In general, giving the vine too easy and comfortable a time – that is, through too much manure, or excessively clean soils without competition from other plants, or planting too widely per hectare – i.e. always giving the soil too much strength – will nurture the vine's leaves excessively, giving rise to a rather feeble and unspirited wine. The vine will not have needed to resort to its full, powerful temperament, to its archetypal force, and so its harvest will not have received the stamp and imprint of its true nature.

These reflections, perhaps almost a little too detailed for amateurs, aim merely to explain why increasing numbers of viticulturists speak more of their fields than of their cellars, as if to underline the grave errors of a past which still very much haunt winegrowing today. Here we tap in to some profound questions: will our agriculture and our knowledge at last begin to ask of the plant – but not impose – a certain degree of effort? It is this human/plant synergy, and not an abstract and solely material body of knowledge, that enables us to participate in the genesis of a great wine.

I beg agricultural colleges to become aware of the arid intellectual state which they too often invoke in their students, the great degree to which they limit these students' creativity, the extent to which they distance them from themselves and their own human qualities. When, one wonders, will they start to teach students to observe life itself, or, for example, the way a vine leaf behaves, pointing earthwards from the moment it appears – quite opposite to, say, a laurel leaf which always points upwards. (See Plates 4 and 5.) We need to grasp that this gesture reveals the leaf's own profound nature.

Surely the time has come to teach students about the personality of each plant, thus enabling them to fully express themselves in a healthy agriculture and to produce foods full of living forces to nourish humanity.

For lovers of wine the important thing to understand is, first of all, the Dionysian nature of the vine, and secondly the need to respect this so that it can connect as well as possible with subtleties of soil and climate – so that, in other words, it can best marry its innate authenticity with the quality of the place where it grows.

A passionate viticulturist will be seeking for something hidden, for knowledge of the underlying forces which invigorate the vine and enable it to imbue its grape with as much force and elegance as possible.

Now that we have staked out the ground we must turn next to a subject fraught with trouble, and ask: What have we done to the vine over the past few decades?

2

Errors in Agriculture

Until the end of the 1950s not all wines were good, far from it, but almost all of them were authentic. Today one could almost feel nostalgia for the bad, real wine! Instead we continually encounter wines where the vine has been prevented from fulfilling its work, and where aesthetic intervention constantly has to labour to produce a good, but soulless, wine by means of technology's thousand artificial measures. Here we find good, false wines, for which the AOC is really just writing on the label rather than a reality in the bottle. The full, original taste, which each 'appellation controlée' once guaranteed to the consumer, no longer exists!

How has this come about? What has happened? It is interesting to see how all this has been astutely orchestrated, and the extent to which producers themselves have been trapped in the process. The viticulturist was first approached with an apparently very attractive product, the herbicide. This was the *vine's first great drama*. A major and laborious task for winegrowers each spring and summer always consisted in keeping their soil free of weeds. (But nowadays the rules have changed as we will see.) This is tiring manual work undertaken during times when nature is flourishing without pause, so naturally a herbicide was tempting. Many tried it out. Those who advised it so insistently took care never to speak of the phenomenon, which scientists call mycorrhiza, so important for wine quality! What is this? Something very simple: to draw in nourishment a root needs the help of micro-organisms in the soil, rather as we need our hands in order to eat. *Each type* of micro-organism allows the root to assimilate *one particular geological aspect* of the soil. In their absence the root starves just as we would if we were sitting at a table full of food with our hands tied behind our back.

The commercial wiliness of the herbicide market consists in the fact that in just a few years it kills almost all the soil's micro-organisms. In the first few years this effect generates confidence in winegrowers since the death of these micro-flora fatten the vine. But after 5 or 8 years little life remains in the soil. If you dig a hole in a soil treated with herbicide for 15 years it is alarming to see how the life which goes to make up the soil has often almost completely disappeared. And of course the roots cannot live there either, and climb back up to the soil's surface (see Plate 6).

Let us translate the consequences of this secret assassination of the soil. When the vine can no longer gain the sustenance it needs from the soil, it becomes possible to sell viticulturists artificial growth agents in massive quantities. This is the *second great drama* of our AOCs, and one that is immensely lucrative for certain interests. A whole new market opens up, one already in existence previously of course, but hitherto fairly modest — that of chemical fertilizers — first for piling on the soil, and then for spraying on the leaves (foliar feed). There's no need to go into the details here, it's enough to understand that a chemical fertilizer is, first and foremost, a salt, and increases the plant's need for water. Just swallow a spoonful of salt and you will feel thirsty, and will need to drink to compensate for this excessive salinity. It is the same for all plants — for instance, a cabbage, once cooked, will give you back all the water it has absorbed.

And of course the effects of these fertilizers are not neutral. Apart from the fact that vines throughout the world, in all possible different locations, are fed in the same way, forcing a plant to absorb too much water is an invitation to nature — which always tries to restore equilibrium — to redress the balance indirectly through diseases. Microbes, viruses or fungal diseases should be regarded as heralds of imbalance or weakness. One day, I hope, this will be written in letters of gold above the gates of all agricultural colleges, which will no longer act as mere agents for the pesticide industry. Microbes and viruses should not be blamed for diseases in agriculture, as one would have us believe. They are merely the executors, the cleaners, like scavenging crabs in the ocean in charge of destroying all that is not sufficiently alive! In combating them without having corrected the imbalance that invokes them, one is just further weakening the whole natural system. To bring about a merely temporary cure, extremely dangerous molecules are applied, which isolate the plant *still more* from the living context it needs to attain its full health. It becomes clear that, in just a few years, we have created the conditions for a still more complex – and more lucrative – condition of incurable disease to manifest.

This slight digression is just to show that chemical fertilizers have led to a strong increase in fungal diseases such as oidium and mildew. These diseases already existed before, of course, but were infinitely less pervasive. The excess water that chemical salts force plants to absorb each time it rains, without respect for the growth that vines can draw from a spring season alone, calls forth fungi that try to regulate this excess water by taking up residence on the leaves. The first consequence of this is that treatments used in the past which were scarcely toxic when used in reasonable doses (Bordeaux mixture and sulphur) are no longer effective enough even when given in far greater concentrations which can, indeed, become toxic. Thus the door is opened to a *third drama* that is very injurious to the quality of our wines.

This is the 'systemic' herbicide. Having found and synthesized new molecules that are as dangerous as they are effective for suppressing the symptoms of these diseases which people doggedly refuse to understand, a process has been invented which *forces the vine to absorb these molecules through its sap*. It's a technical stroke of genius, for disease simply cannot appear! But in qualitative terms it's very serious. Let us try to understand the significance of what has happened.

Until the 1970s these dangerous artificial molecules remained on the surfaces of leaves and fruit: rain washed them off, and the consumer could get rid of them easily enough by rinsing. This polluted rivers but not the food itself too much. The new process now forces these dangerous molecules into the very sap itself in less than an hour. Very practical, but these poisons — which are so toxic that the viticulturist who sprays them is legally required to wear a sealed suit with breathing mask — pass right into the plant's interior. It takes only a little imagination and understanding to see that, in the sap, they are going to pass into and help form our fruits and vegetables! The poisoned vine is supposed to eliminate these poisons within two months, if all goes well. But the toxicity of some of these products is so great that just 2 or 3 ml placed in an egg would instantly kill a beech marten that eats it. The dosage used in viticulture, we should state, is several litres per hectare.

In addition, no one thought to tell winegrowers that sap is the vine's principal connection with the sun or the solar system, thus to all that gives rise to taste, life, the forces of ageing and maturation! It is evident that poisoned sap — and this is not putting it too strongly — cannot accomplish the same qualitative work.

Due to all these dramas, sometimes still heralded as progress, we have now arrived at a situation of abundant harvests, certainly, but bearing little imprint either of the soil that has been so weakened, or the unique climatic conditions which the sap does not properly absorb; and thus bearing little of its AOC distinction!

This brief summary does not allow us to enter too far into further important details. But what we should understand also is the qualitative impoverishment that plant cloning leads to. Each type of vine – Chenin, Chardonnay, Cabernet etc. – bears thousands of original qualities unequally distributed in each wine stock. This is why, when replanting vines in the past, so-called 'massal' selection was used, which involved taking cuttings from hundreds of stocks, each one the bearer of different virtues, and using them to recreate a bigger population. In the case of each clone, by contrast, one sole stock was isolated instead, usually a very productive one, and the bearer of one or two clearly apparent aromatic qualities – but this overlooked the fact that beauty really only arises where a multiplicity of different characteristics create an equilibrium together, the one offsetting or complementing the action of another. This one stock was thus multiplied into hundreds of thousands or even millions of plants. Even if several clones per grape variety are now selected, the problem remains more or less the same. In addition, considerably increased yields have obliged growers to make 'green harvests', that is, to get rid of a surfeit of grapes before they are fully ripe. These current practices, far from highlighting serious errors of selection, are nowadays regarded as a positive development! In industrial-scale production, clones are seen as great progress. Deriving from the same originating stock, all these descendants flower at the same time and can thus also be harvested at the same time, even by machine. But from another point of view, that of full complexity of expression of the variety which each type of wine represents, this is real impoverishment. It is rather like a discussion on some subject or other in which either just one, or 30 people are involved, all with their different characters and perspectives. The monologue will certainly not lead to the same depth and scope. The clone which has reigned supreme for 30 years has impoverished the capacity of our grape varieties to express their full depth or abundance of taste.

Let us end this chapter by stating, quite simply, that a wine bearing little of the characteristics of its place of origin is hard to market if it has not been, let us say, 'overlaid'. Thus the gate has been opened to the *fourth and last drama of the vine,* whereby winegrowers, who had by now become prisoners of a system which often costs them between 1,000 and 1,500 euros per hectare per year* in artificial measures, were offered almost irresistible 'remedies'. Technology has thus come to dominate our AOC wines, at the same time leading to their devaluation and destruction.

France, so rich in regional qualities and in micro-climate was thus poised to lose its loveliest adornment in exchange for selling its wines throughout the world and submitting to all the implications of global competition.

---

* Between approximately £650 and £1,000.

3

The Cellar

So much has been written on the subject of the cellar or *cave*, that in what follows I am going to emphasize what has generally not been said.

The basic rule is simple: when the growth of the grape between spring and autumn is the pure product of nature, in other words when the vine, with all its originality of character and variety can, in its own way, transform meteorological influences into cellulose, starch and sugar without being interrupted by toxic artificial molecules, or artificial chemical growth enhancers, the 'must' possesses a kind of harmony or equilibrium which enables it to mature well in the cellar. All viticulturists who practise healthy cultivation can confirm this. Naturally there are still some basic simple actions to be taken, such as stirring the lees, and racking or decanting. But fundamentally, if you leave the vine to get on with its work, and still better if you actively help it in this task (and this requires a macrocosmic understanding of life as we will see later), if your vineyards are well situated and your grape varieties are well adapted to it, the cellar is just a kind of midwifery, nothing more nor less, to help things take their proper course.

There are, it is true, a few little secrets, and hardly more than that, relating to pressing times, cuvaison (maceration of the grape skins), or the period of contact with the lees. It is true that these actions have tangible effects, but overall there is little that needs doing in the cellar, except to observe with admiration what is underway. Nor is there much surprising or innovative in this. It is just a return to the situation which prevailed for many centuries, up to the end of the 1940s or '50s, when an agriculture that was still based on a balanced understanding of nature enabled the great vineyards to produce wines that were still majestic one hundred years later.

If, in contrast, one tries to replace nature without understanding her, if one thinks, as was still being taught a few years ago in the biggest wine-growing regions, that the soil is a dead substrate, of small importance, the wine deriving from a truly 'denatured' vine will become so precarious at the cellar that continuous, costly supervision and intervention will be essential. And there is really little point in astonishment at the unreasonable behaviour of the must in the cellar, unless one also expresses astonishment at the often murderous agricultural methods applied to the vines themselves. It is only by accepting this latter view that one can really maintain that the cellar's work is essential to produce some kind of half-decent wine ...

In fact one can characterize, and perhaps caricature, two different paths in viticulture: one which relies on replacing nature, and thus the AOC, obliging the cellar to fabricate a good taste, but without much characteristic distinction, and in which only one cloned variety can still be recognized; and the other, in which, by hearkening fully to the vine and the life of the *terroir* where it grows, one allows it to unfold and flourish in the loveliest way possible. This just means that it can seize hold of the original qualities generated by a landscape, by particular animals, by various agricultural measures – all of which, as we will see, are rounded into a whole by biodynamics. Thus, as viticulturists, we can choose whether to become industrialized 'wine makers' or, instead, 'nature's assistants'.

To sum up our view of the right approach to adopt in the cellar, we therefore need to take a step backwards and examine in detail each one of our agricultural measures. We have already discussed how, from a non-material, intangible realm, photosynthesis creates noble matter in the grape. To deepen this aspect it is essential to understand how one can limit the work of the cellar. The climate is composed of three constituents which every year produce multiple variations. First the rain, either coming early, or slow to arrive, either abundant or sparse; then the heat, also subject to the same qualifying differences; and finally the wind, or air in movement, itself linked to the quality of light into which play the landscape's attributes: in particular, light-reflecting lakes or rivers. And all this diversifies any uniform continuity. Heat, for example, can quickly transform humidity into a passing mist or allow it to ferment in soils for a longer period. Winds participate in this task in a different way on each occasion. The Greeks had seven gods of the wind, of whom Zephyr was the gentlest. Yet again we see how past wisdom sharpens our faculties for perceiving subtle qualities, which in ancient times were embodied in the form of divinities. In a somewhat similar way the river Rhône in France is referred to locally as 'Doctor Mistral'!

And it is this rich diversity and complexity which affects soils, the mycorhiza and photosynthesis. Everything the vine creates each year as shoots, leaves and grapes is marked by these innumerable subtleties that are never identical from one vintage year to another. And all this passes through the grape pulp in which the grape pips are enfolded, and contracts and focuses in them as in a synthesis. All plants work primarily to ensure the survival of their species, of their offspring. This genesis of the seed is an extraordinary thing. Goethe has revealed it to us in his poetry. After immersing itself in the physical world, and each year recreating itself wholly or in part, the plant has this capacity to contract to the minutest degree and to disappear into its seed – which will now bear its essence, all its knowledge and experience, until it unfolds again the following spring.

This process of contraction cannot properly begin until the plant has finished flowering. For the vine, so closely connected with the four seasons, it is ideal if this genesis of the seed does not occur until after the midsummer solstice, when days start to grow shorter again.

Flowering too early sets the vine at odds with the temporal rhythms with which it is so connected. Until the summer solstice, as days grow longer, the prevailing forces are centrifugal. In other words, as days grow longer and the sun's attraction stronger, nature increasingly expands, drawing the plant world outwards and upwards. These forces help the vine to construct its physical body. Only when the days start to shorten, and prevailing forces start to descend back into the earth instead, becoming centripetal, can the vine begin to contract and produce its fruit and seeds. Flowering too early runs counter to these forces and often produces a wine that is promising at the first taste but very disappointing at the second. The fruit and seed will form, certainly, but will not properly bear within them the rhythms of the seasons. It would be interesting to organize a wine-tasting session on this theme — on condition, of course, that a healthy agriculture, unburdened by any technology, is allowed to participate. Thus the pulp of the grape can be seen as the 'bath' in which this seed forms, each time bearing in itself subtly different nuances. Steiner tells us that in the vine, some of the forces destined for the pip remain in the pulp, and that this explains its predilection for often explosive fermentation, and the poor capacity of the pips to produce a new vine stock.

All this goes to show that each year the vine is imprinted with the caprices or chaos of the weather, a little like a painter who is given different colours each time and produces a different quality of portrait upon his canvas.

The vine's labour is to use all the aspects of climate in a season, and all the variations of the life of the soil, to compose an overall, unified image. As artist of the earth it will always try to create coherence and harmony, even if certain elements imposed on it don't necessarily suit its preference. But to manage this, its archetypal force should not be hampered or obstructed by insensitive interventions. This is what goes to make a vintage. And this is why, even if the year and the climate have been poor, a vintage year can nevertheless be great. This is also why, for example, acidity or alcohol levels, which analysis shows to be excessive or inadequate, may be unnoticeable in the taste. A healthy agriculture enables these factors to be included and subsumed in a 'globality'. Just as a certain somewhat vivid colour can find its fitting place in the overall context of a painting, so the quasi totality of vintages can come to full expression. But this, of course, only on one condition: that life itself be respected! This insight shows why official winetasting sessions, to confirm that the AOC label is a true indicator of the bottle's contents, are actually so absurd. The requirement nowadays for obtaining the AOC designation is no longer the full expression of the AOC, but rather a 'correct' and perfectly nice wine – although one that has no location-related quality!

We have to know how to help the vine to express itself, and to do so we first need to understand the extent of its capacities, so that we can keep our work in the cellar to a minimum. The first step in this direction is to practise organic growing methods. As we will see, biodynamics takes us still further.

The vital thing that I am trying to convey here, dear wine lovers, is that if one has not interfered in the work of composition that the vine itself knows how to complete during spring and summer — if leaves, flowers and roots have been allowed to communicate freely with their surroundings so as to respond to increasingly varied situations — and if, of course, yields have remained reasonable: if, if and if ... then each vintage will be worthy of the name without any technological aid to adulterate it!

But just imagine a situation, a very common one in fact, where the soil cannot nourish the roots, the leaves receive foliar feeds, where chemical salts force the vine to drink when it should no longer be growing, where poisonous molecules fill the sap which has to try to eliminate them as swiftly as possible, where 20 percent of leaves are removed artificially six weeks before harvest to 'aid ripening' (!), where the fruits tend to rot on the branch without ripening through lack of life forces and are sprayed three or four times with anti-rot treatment! Well, we will all agree that the 'work' will not be able to proceed with much coherence, and the behaviour of the juice at the cellar will no longer be embedded in the wise, structuring forces which nature dispenses *freely* if we respect her. Thus the cellar becomes a factory and the viticulturist a 'wine maker'.

In this situation we are going to have to intervene all the

time. First one needs to add yeast because the natural yeasts that arise in the course of the year have been killed off. One will have to go out and buy yeast that has often been produced by processes closely related to gene technology. In certain cases a wily commercial sense will even allow one to avoid this appearing on the label, since this isn't required if the added gene belongs to the 'family' of those already present. It is quite easy to imagine the commercial pressures that are brought to bear to obtain this kind of 'family right'! There is such a widespread and prevalent lack of understanding in viticulture today that it is often regarded as proof of professionalism to say that yeast has been systematically added to wines to avoid natural yeasts, which, it is added in all seriousness, 'lead to a bad taste'! Few winegrowers realize that when one modifies a musical chord with an alien element it becomes a dissonance; and that similarly, adulterating a wine with absurd practices leads to disharmony. Instead people are very easily tempted by the innumerable (over 300) aromatic yeasts, which in-depth economic studies have shown will persuade the consumer – of whatever social class, at whatever price range and in every country – to make a purchase. A consultant will be able to advise such things as: 'The banana-taste yeast did very well in Japan for 5-euro wines, but now try the one which produces a blackcurrant taste.' Yes, indeed, we are talking about AOC wines here, and not just table wines – which would be less shocking. The full palette of tastes is gathered here and made available to viti-

culturists, and can even be generated via a computer programme. But, as you will agree, press articles revealing these
practices are extremely rare!

Yet if, through lack of understanding, one has embarked on
this path which will inevitably lead to smaller businesses
collapsing, one has to become highly interventionist and
continually fuss around the patient, keeping it alive with
additions of yeasts and enzymes, through osmosis, tempera-
ture control, etc. One has to be permanently on guard to limit
the aggression of all these living agents (bacteria) etc. which
sense that a wine of 'poor birth' is their rightful prey, from
which they *have* to nourish themselves in order to play their
role. When life's proper equilibrium is destroyed or rendered
perilous, the resulting produce is fragile too, and the aid of
cosmetic adulteration or technology becomes indispensable.
In contrast, by reinforcing the descent and assimilation of life
forces into and by the vine – and this is what biodynamics
excels at – the grape filled with these forces can cope with
almost any of the viticulturist's eccentricities. You will now
understand why people hold such differing views about the
work which is needed at the cellar.

Let me give another example: what one could call the
indispensable heat phase of fermentation which, for a few
days, needs to climb to 26° or even 30°. This phase can be
considered on the one hand either as potential decay, or on
the other as an indispensable factor in achieving wine's full
expression. Fermentation is like a fever, the search for a new

balance through excess of heat. It is not so long ago that people regarded fever as a healing process. Today we fear or disdain it and try simply to dispel it, thus distancing medicine from the healing forces which often accompany it.* Fermentation has suffered the same fate, and nowadays people dislike the bother of hearkening each year to the different instructions which the grape issues about its state. They limit the risks without understanding that if agriculture has provided good conditions for the vines, the heat phase will enable grapes to reveal additional qualities in the wine.

Nor can one overlook the role of osmosis, since it is now used so much. This means concentrating the must by removing water, in order to enhance the tastes that the vine has not been able to bring to full expression. This lack of understanding extends to saying that this is done to suppress the effect of the last rainfall, considered undesirable. But this is to overlook the fact that when a soil is not full of chemical salts — if the earth filters its rains through proper microbial life, and if the roots of the vine have not been curbed in their descent by these dreadful synthetic molecules, and can delve downwards for metres — rainfall will very rarely hamper the vintage. And even if 100 millimetres of rain has fallen in a few days, biodynamic methods can still, certainly, achieve an interesting wine, obliging the vine to exhale this water by

---

* Of course, fever can be dangerous to a patient if it rises too high, but a moderate fever can, as symptom of the body's own self-healing forces, accompany and aid the healing process.

treating it with a quartz (silica) based remedy. If agriculture is healthy, a vine and its grapes will not gorge themselves on water but will drink *reasonable* amounts. It really isn't normal for an AOC wine to be subjected to osmosis; but if this is done (being legal nowadays), 'wine concentrate' ought to be printed on the label, as on cheap orange juice. What consumers can assume is an exceptional year, in which dry conditions and sunshine have married well, is sometimes just due to reverse osmosis which, let's not forget, reverses the wine's natural polarity — and with what consequences for the ageing of the wine? It also opens the door to excessive yields. The aim here is not to examine every single detail of this almost industrial-scale viticulture, which even sometimes affects very costly wines and which spreads a little further every day thanks to the adroit hand of the Institut National des Appellations d'Origine (INAO).* What I am endeavouring to do, rather, is to explain in fairly simple terms to people of good will that all these artificial methods are chiefly linked to ever-increasing agricultural errors.

Let us, finally, take the example of micro-oxygenation. This new hobbyhorse just replaces the work that the leaves of the wine should do for the grape if agriculture was healthy. And in this latter case the practice is useless. All these increasing errors have their consequences in the cellar. The centrifugal forces will try to expel synthetic molecules that have been

---

* National institute of the 'Appelations d'Origine'.

forced into the sap, and in doing so will destabilize the wine. The enzymes nourish the yeasts that are not adapted to the specific conditions of the year, etc. etc. I do not wish to condemn a producer who chooses this course, but only to tell him that as far as wine technology is concerned France really has nothing to export. Too many countries with readily available cheap labour can achieve exactly the same taste at a quarter of the cost or less. And if we fail to understand this, commercial collapse will follow swiftly. No region is protected from this danger! Let us not forget that in 2005 the government of France had to dispose of 1.5 million hectolitres of AOC wine that had not been sold. In addition, all these practices and many others tarnish the image other countries have of France and its wines a little more each day. Our diversities of climate and geology, perfectly adapted to our grape varieties, ought potentially to ensure that we are almost beyond the reach of global competition. I don't wish to imply that French wines are the only ones worth considering, but in France we do have the resources of a viticulture which is, rightly, the envy of many others.

Fortunately another kind of viticulture exists, still very dispersed, but one which increasingly understands the traps that have been set for it. It is returning to 'real wines' where the word 'terroir'* which has become so debased today, is

---

* Translated literally as *soil*, this French term describes not only the terrain on which the vines are grown, but also encompasses soil, slope, orientation to the sun, elevation and effects of climate.

regaining a little of its true meaning. In fact, in allowing all these artificial measures, in using them too much, a space has, paradoxically, been opened for those who want to go in a different direction. The less credulous customer is starting to discover the truth that has been hidden from him. Is it really worth going into ecstasies about the 'nose' or the taste of violets in a wine if one knows this has been added through aromatic yeasts? This question is one which needs to be asked clearly! To accelerate this return to real wines it would be enough to require by law the publication on every label of the technological practices involved in producing the wine. For example, this might read: 'wine concentrated by osmosis and perfumed with artificial yeast X, which gives a nose of violet.' Of course this will never happen, since too many interests are at stake in the commercial wine world. But it has been possible, by contrast, to form a group which gives a *legal guarantee of the authenticity of the taste of the AOC.* This group has existed for five years now and today includes 120 viti-culturists in 10 countries, and has met with great success in all continents. You will find details of this association in the Appendix. In speaking of real wines we need to give a very precise definition of this, with a very strict charter of quality — also in the Appendix — which lists all the actions prohibited both in the vineyards and in the cellars. Such a charter will give consumers not just virtuous words but *a legal commit-ment on the part of the viticulturist* relating to his vines, his wine and the consumer. Subsequently it is necessary for the wine to achieve a certain level of quality and originality. The group's aim is to show, 'glass in hand', that in different locations grape varieties express themselves differently in each case, and that it is these subtleties, unmasked by cosmetic measures, which endow a wine with its own innate charm. A wine should not just be 'biodynamic' but it also needs to be good, imprinted with the originality of the place it comes from, and by the labour of a well-adapted grape variety.

On the path towards real wines there are of course very different levels of commitment and achievement, with fairly recent dates of conversion to organic or biodynamic agriculture, and widely varying results. Sometimes the will is there but not yet the results. It is common to hear those who want to get on board this new market without taking rigorous decisions saying that they are '95%' organic or biodynamic. Just a moment's reflection will show the vacuousness of such a phrase. As James Milton, a remarkable biodynamic viticulturist in New Zealand, joked: 'Can you say a woman is 95% pregnant?' One also hears people saying that they use very few artificial herbicides, just enough 'to save vines from disease' ... without understanding that it is these same herbicides which over time create the conditions for disease.

Ideally we need to allow human beings to live and sleep — the time when all defences vanish — in an environment where solar forces predominate. Of course there are exceptions, such as some monasteries, usually Cistercian ones, which are intentionally located in very 'terrestrial' places, so that the human being's thinking and will can substitute themselves for solar forces. The permanent meditative effort involved enables people to develop capacities they might otherwise not. It is also necessary to rediscover the forces generated by each shape or form via frequencies called 'form waves' – different in each case, and producing qualitative effects which are always very specific. Each shape generates specific frequencies or micro-frequencies and wave lengths, a knowledge which architecture of the past made full use of. Domes, vaults and other forms used very specific proportions and rules to generate forces beneficial to the human being, Everything on earth is subject to underlying numerical laws. We can even see this in chemical reactions. Why for instance do two atoms of hydrogen link with one atom of oxygen to make H_2O? To learn at school that H_2O is water without learning about the underlying forces that unite them is already a first step in denying a knowledge of life forces, and in ensuring that winegrowers later resort to chemicals without much thought. Some frequencies are not benevolent but highly destructive, such as high-tension cables, mobile phone antennae, etc. These dangerous frequencies are apparently being used to develop a new generation of secret weapons, while the healing ones – for example in alternative and homeopathic medicines – are increasingly outlawed in France. We are now faced with a situation in which man-made appliances are interfering with the natural, life-generating frequencies of the solar system, thus having a detrimental effect on life forces. This brings us back to the extraordinary wisdom embedded in the so-called Platonic forms of the tetrahedron, cube, octahedron (double pyramid), icosahedron and dodecahedron. Each of these bears specific forces related to corresponding planetary impulses. Other, simpler forms comprise precise proportions of breadth and height that generate very beneficial effects for the human being and life. An arch corresponding to these laws always re-establishes balance in relation to the ground's tug of gravity. Houses under which the negative energy of a stream flows used to be constructed with an underground vault to allow life to remain healthy above ground. An underground stream generates negative energies because it disturbs the balance between negative and positive ions and creates radon gas. This radon phenomenon can even lead to death where the direction of the stream is opposite to that of the sun, i.e. West to East. No cathedral was ever built without several water courses in the foundations which all cross under the place where the altar is situated, and above which an arch is constructed. The rising negative current is reflected at ground level by the vault in such a way that these two negative aspects become a positive one. One could also mention the labyrinths designed by Leonardo da Vinci, or Dürer, or Chartres Cathedral, which highlight this mastery which once existed over the world of energies always present behind the material world.

If you talk to estate agents they will tell you that out of 50 or 60 houses there are often one or two which are regularly put back on the market. They are located in places with excessively negative energy. Some people, particularly women, have retained this sensitivity which allows them to feel either better or worse in a house, depending on its location, its forms and materials, and even its past history. All this belongs to the realm of 'geobiology'.

It is important to consider these factors in viticulture. These qualities of invisible, but very real energies also affect our wine. Too much time spent in a place where one does not feel well can lead to severe illnesses. The same applies to a cellar in an 'inappropriate' place which can exert a negative effect on the wine – where the laws of life succumb to an excess of telluric forces. This occurs sometimes in very small areas of a few square metres, where it always proves necessary to maintain fermentation with the aid of a neighbouring barrel, or rack it (draw it off) to regain a fresher taste. In contrast there are some ancient cellars, imbued with the wisdom and knowledge of long-gone winegrowers, which can 'swallow' or reharmonize the imbalances in the must without anyone having to do anything. Every viticulturist aware of the laws of life will have interesting stories about such things.

Many of the finest modern cellars, which sometimes represent huge investments, are quite absurd in terms of energies. Simply on the subject of electrical pollution – i.e. at 50/60 hertz, which emits 50 or 60 vibrations per second to everything it comes in contact with, including cement, from an electric wire or even an unlit bulb – one finds situations which really make one want to shake the architect or the owner! While the electric part of the electro-magnetic field can be easily resolved through a good earthing system (which usually deteriorates within a few years) its magnetic part, which is more perverse, is sometimes impossible to cure. In former times people only put low voltage cables (25 volts) or continuous current in cellars. *Poor yeasts, summon your courage to battle with all these obstacles!*

All this is connected with technological aids.

Dear wine lovers, please reflect on your own wine cellars too – I'm thinking in particular of certain bottle fridges which too often emit 50/60 magnetic hertz! And please, above all, do not buy one of those electric field detectors since their sensitivity is sometimes greatly reduced in order to calm your suspicions. Also avoid too much metal in a wine cellar which, together with today's hertz saturation, sets up resonances with all sorts of rhythms injurious to our real, living wines. Such effects may greatly modify their ageing properties …

Yes, indeed, the situation today is a good deal more complex than it used to be, for the human being is creating and imposing on our earth, and the whole environment, all sorts of artificial frequencies without considering the interference this represents to the frequencies which sustain life! Solar energies do not arrive on earth via lorries and labourers but through multiple frequencies, each of which has precise functions. To fill, or rather saturate the atmosphere with frequencies created for our electrical goods will come to modify what Kepler called the 'music of the spheres' – that is, all the system of harmonious energies which gives life to the earth. Without these it will become a mere corpse. Failing to understand this is, at the same time, to alter the climate and the human being. We must see the earth not as an isolated entity but as embedded in a dynamic macrocosm and inter-penetrating systems of forces.

When planet earth is exhausted or reaches the end of a cycle, it recharges itself by inverting its polarities. More con-cretely, this means that the North pole reverses and becomes the South pole. This is sometimes referred to as a 'pole-shift'. Scientists know that it has already happened several times in history. (By drilling in soil with iron magnetite it is possible to discover, depending on the soil's depth, what was prevailing as the North/South pole at the time.) It is possible for the lengthy cycle to be shortened by mankind's activities, parti-cularly in relation to our effect on the energies in the atmos-phere. In this respect it is important to go beyond the notion of 'global warming', and see that we are facing the first steps of a pole-shift. We do not know how quickly this inversion can take place. It may take a century or it may happen sud-denly in a few days. Another uncertainty involves the possi-bility that, once the energy polarities of the earth have changed or are in the process of changing, the physical body of the earth might follow. In other words, the physical North pole could become the South pole. This is not science fiction, but a real possibility, studied seriously by some scientists. When studying the earth, one should consider that it is a living organism. This calls for a unified, holistic thinking — one that can combine various disciplines and data and reveal the truth that lies behind them. In the same way, it is important to see that an earthquake is not, as we are often told, simply caused by two tectonic plates that touch — just as a smile is not just two lips stretching. What is significant is to know the person who stretches his lips into a smile.

Steiner said once that the earth is like an elephant. For years it can put up with being treated poorly, and then suddenly it might break its chains. An understanding can be achieved only if the earth is conceived as a living system with veins of specific energies running across it. This was known or intuited in former times, and the location of great architecture and significant religious landmarks of the past can indicate such knowledge.

Nowadays too many people are captives of the dogma which says that life is born from matter. In fact the reverse is true. Our good earth and its forces of gravity serve to densify and manifest physically all that enters into their sphere of activity. It's as simple as that. It is not the soil which makes the plant but, first and foremost, the plant which makes the soil and humus by condensing the intangible. This lack of understanding for the world of energies and the innumerable waves and frequencies of which it is composed, may become perilous in forthcoming years, and generate processes which will dwarf such things as asbestos poisoning or contaminated blood supplies. Can one place one's ear to one of the frequencies of 900 or 1800 million vibrations per second without thereby modifying the whole behaviour of one's brain cells – which also have their rhythms and their susceptibilities? Existing studies on mobile phones (cell phones) have been suspended, and the budgets supposedly allocated for their review have been linked to a change of protocol, in order to demonstrate that they are non-repeatable – and can therefore be ignored, provisionally at least.*

This is the nature of our times. Did you know that no insurance company will cover possible injury from a mobile?

To return to physical forms and their particular forces, each one thus generates specific frequencies called form waves. All this knowledge informed the architecture of the past up to a few centuries ago, and can now be measured and quantified. This enables us to understand the forms of wine barrels.

The barrel is in fact a permanent arch: just climb into one, or if you're too big, into a 600-litre vat, where it will be more comfortable to experience a few happy moments. Diogenes wasn't crazy!† An animal less imprisoned by its intellect than us knows this instinctively. A dog will eagerly exchange its

---

* See studies by Dr. Roger Santini at: www.next-up.org

† Diogenes of Sinope (412–323 BC), Greek philosopher known as 'the Cynic'. He once famously took a tub (depicted as a barrel by John William Waterhouse's painting) for an abode.

basket for a barrel. Birds do not construct square nests. Their eggs are not cuboid, nor are the honeycomb cells of bees. One can also understand the shape of certain church roofs in this way which, inverted, give us the form of an amphora – in which wine is very much at home, although in a different way from a barrel.

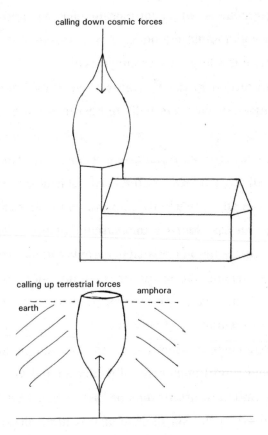

Appealing to and connecting with the world of above or below does not exert the same effect on a wine. We need to rediscover this knowledge to avoid constructing both buildings and containers in any arbitrary way and with any arbitrary material. Each person's creativity should first of all be nourished through knowledge of the laws to which the earth and the human being are subject. Without this, creation risks becoming savage, devoid of meaning and cold, and may generate people who are appallingly dangerous. To take one example, in cases where authorities have permitted the installation of mobile phone antennae on storage facilities, our sensitive drinking water, on which we depend for life, is being bombarded by death-bearing sub-natural frequencies. What impact, one wonders, will this have on human beings in the future?

We also need to regain an understanding of the sun and its effects at different places on the earth, and of the positions where it rises and sets at particular moments, i.e. the summer and winter solstice, or, one can say, the day when solar forces triumph over the laws of gravity and vice versa. This may help us to comprehend the shape of the foundations of house locations up to two or three centuries ago, which varied according to latitude. The further south we go the more we find a long rectangle (which ends with a line at right angles to the equator). The further north we go, in contrast, the more the rectangle becomes first a square and then a north-south orientated rectangle. Why mention this here? Because one finds very similar laws governing different forms given in the past to barrels, depending on the latitude of their provenance. At Porto, for example, the barrels are longer than in Burgundy,

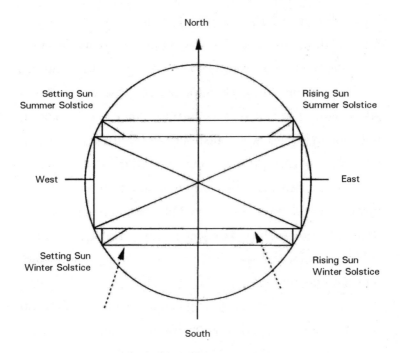

The four angles of these shapes are linked to the rising and setting of the sun at a specific latitude.

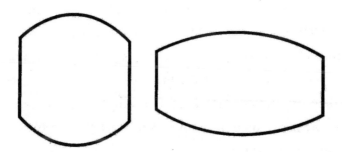

Traditional barrel shapes: the further south one travels (in the Northern Hemisphere) the longer the barrel's shape.

for these reasons. Thus during its genesis wine was in harmony with the real energies at work in a particular location.

In the past this knowledge of energies was not just understood but intuitively experienced. One can probably also extend it to different forms given to vessels containing milk, oil and water, which no doubt connected with the body of energies of each product and improved their conservation. You see, our sensory nervous system only connects us to the physical world, but not the world of energies from which we derive life forces. Thus, basing everything on physical matter, we cut ourselves off from life. For the past two centuries the only laws taught in science have been those accessible to the cerebral world, and thus those of matter. Previously it was the opposite: only the energies really counted. Today we urgently need to reconnect these two forms of knowledge and thus to liberate a large part of the scientific world from the cul-de-sac in which its materialistic dogmas have imprisoned it. It is time to place these countless and respectable discoveries gained through laborious investigation of matter into a wider context in which the physical aspect is just part of the reality. We need first of all to realize that all our sensory perceptions isolate us because they keep returning us to our separate identity and individuality, which feels itself to be physically divided from all that surrounds us.

What is absolutely true at a physical level is far less so when we come to fields of energy, where every impulse impacts on its surroundings without the watchful guard of an individual, physical barrier. Observing a young child can help us grasp this. As long as he is not yet wholly subject to earthly laws – look into his eyes to see this – he can still perceive the realities of the energies underlying matter, a world to which we are denied access by our sensory perceptions, which simultaneously enable our distinct and separate individuality to develop. Once the earth has adapted the child to its terrestrial laws of individuality (gravity), he will start to say 'I' in reference to himself, instead of calling himself by his first name without full awareness of his distinct self. 'Peter likes blackberries' thus becomes 'I like blackberries' around the age of 3. This is also when the child loses his clairvoyance, that is to say his perception of non-physical things. The animal who has not acquired full individuality since he is subject to his species – which is why every member of a species is nearly identical – is thus less isolated from this living system of energies and has full, though unconscious, access to it. This is how the beaver constructs a dam using mathematical laws it is unaware of. It is this which enables animals to sense danger, or find water from kilometres away.

We have already seen something similar in Chapter 1 with the myth of Dionysus. The Egyptians also referred to this terrestrial state in speaking of Isis who was desolate as she searched everywhere on earth for Osiris who had been torn to pieces by Typhon. Typhon symbolizes gravity. Here again we have an image of the incarnation of matter, and our separation from an overall context of energies through gravitational laws. Isis, one can say, tries to find on earth each small piece of a puzzle which, at the level of energies previously formed a whole, beautiful image named Osiris. This puzzle, fiendishly difficult to resolve, relates very much to the search in agriculture and viticulture for ways to produce a true and great wine. Material science cannot advance unless its knowledge is bedded back into a much wider context than the limits within which it lies fragmented today. Without this, indeed, it will become dramatically dangerous, as genetic engineering has already shown us, with its tendency to believe that the 'bad' gene is responsible for lack of equilibrium which has arisen by 'unlucky chance'. No one tries to understand why the system of energies acts in a different way in one case or another. Instead people hold fast to the fact that, to promote what is best, they need to suppress what is unwelcome. Nor is any consideration given to the reaction of an animal that responds immediately to genetic engineering by developing disease such as leukaemia or, if you prefer, to a disorganizing influence with a disorganizing reaction. On the contrary, attempts are even being made to prevent leukaemia through genetics. And yet we will have to learn, with suffering and sorrow perhaps, that the only thing enabling us to avoid the terrible degeneracy of our immense materialism will be knowledge of complementarities linked to a more global definition of the laws of earthly life. It is this understanding alone that will bring about true and lasting progress in agri-

Solar forces of attraction,
forces of levity

Warmth: fruit-forming energy. The degree
of connection with heat-forces leads to a
varying fruit-forming capacity

Light: flowering energy. The degree of
connection with light-forces leads to a
varying flowering capacity

Liquid: leaf energy. The degree of
connection with water-forces leads to
varying leaf sizes

Mineral: root energy. The degree of
connection with gravitational-forces leads
to a varying capacity for penetrating the soil

Forces of terrestrial attraction,
forces of gravity

Plate 1: The four states of matter

Plate 2: The nettle concentrates 'heat' and 'light' forces in its leaves

Plate 3: Through its very strong connection with heat-forces, the cypress tree reveals a wholly upward-rising growth gesture, which does not permit any branch to extend horizontally. This is a perfect illustration of what the Greeks called an 'Apollonian' plant

Plate 4: Laurel leaves are literally 'drawn' upwards, showing a strong connection with solar attraction (the 'Apollonian' plant)

Plate 5: The vine. The uppermost leaves extend horizontally. A few days after emerging these turn downwards again, demonstrating what the Greeks called a 'Dyonisian' plant, or a plant strongly dominated by gravitational-forces

Plate 6: Roots from a vine that was given weed killer after roughly 10–12 years. One can see clearly how its roots then had to grow towards the surface of the soil to feed themselves on fertilizers

Plate 7: A church spire (Copenhagen)

Plate 8: Stirring the biodynamic preparations: creating a vortex

Plate 9: The rose, showing its spiral form

Plates 10 and 11: A spiral in the vine and a spiral in the priest's mitre

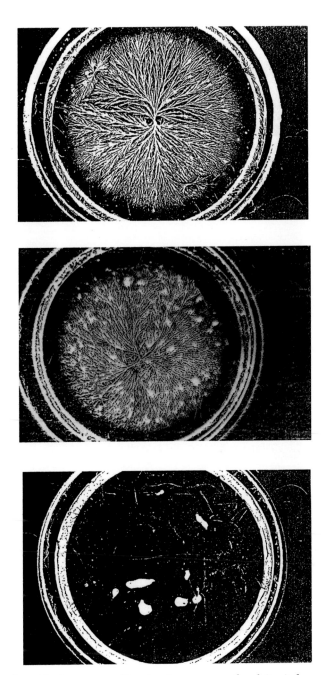

Plate 12: Sugar crystallization images: unrefined (top), brown (middle), white (bottom). The crystallization image clearly shows that white sugar is a dead product. The copper chloride process has not been organised by life forces, but instead dries up in a heap or spot

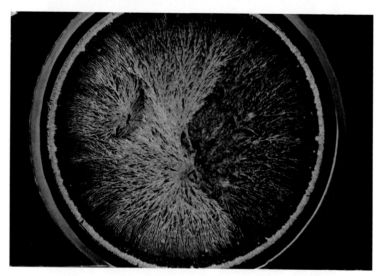

Plate 13: *Crystallization images of strawberries; a traditional type (top), and a new variety grown using organic methods. Despite organic farming, the bottom photo indicates poor life-force organization, with no structure or centre. The bio-engineering involved in the development of this new kind of strawberry indicates negative effects at the energy level*

Plate 14:

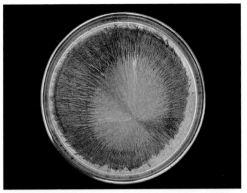

Very good crystallization image of white wine, showing excellent structure and detail, as well as a precise centre

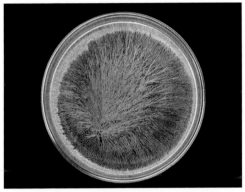

The same wine after passing under a barcode reader. The pattern now shows distinct areas of weakness

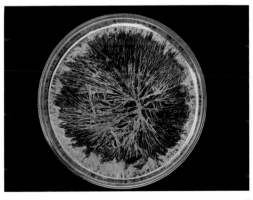

Poor crystallization image of a wine produced using modern farming methods and artificial techniques in the cellar

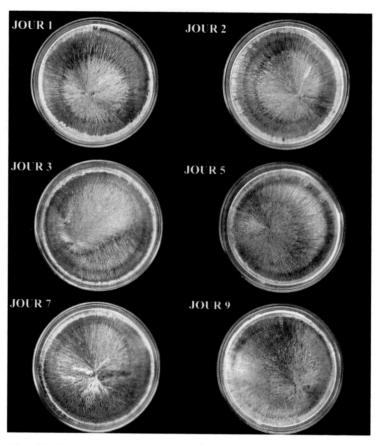

Plate 15: Biodynamic wine resists the forces of destruction at work in the process of oxidation, studied for 9 consecutive days. The bottle is uncorked and half full. From the seventh day onwards one can see zones of weakness in the life-force organization

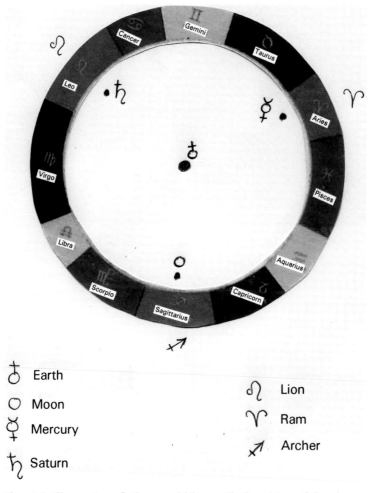

♂	Earth	♌	Lion
○	Moon	♈	Ram
☿	Mercury	♐	Archer
♄	Saturn		

Plate 16: Illustration of what would be an ideal position of the planets in relation to the earth for the vine. One does not need such a theoretical situation to benefit from the planets' positive effects

Plate 17: The importance of dates for harvesting and planting: identical vines, cut and planted in the same soil at an interval of several days

Lettuces planted on either light (blossom) or water (leaf) days, at an interval of several days. Those where a 'light' impulse (left) has reinforced the flowering process have started bolting much earlier (the stem is thick and growing strongly upwards, so these lettuces are no longer fit for sale). The other batch, sown under a water (leaf) impulse, have rounded out nicely and have no main stem inside them

culture, in such a way that the laws of the physical world can be connected to the surrounding world of energies. This path already lies open and it is called biodynamics. Each day it reveals its results in wine a little more, and will bring about a different approach in agriculture since its qualitative effects are undeniable, proven and without any injurious side effect. Biodynamic agriculture is extraordinarily economical, especially if one factors in the enormous costs for social benefit payments linked to dietary deficiencies. And it is these last arguments which, for commercial reasons, have made it an enemy to beat down at any price. It has been called sectarian, something clearly refuted in legal proceedings (and by courageous journalists). Then it has been declared something 'for the wealthy' despite the fact that it is employed by many small viticulturists and in developing countries. It has been called 'esoteric', since it works with very tiny material quantities. If biodynamics is esoteric, however, because one cannot explain its effects in purely physical terms, then a mobile phone or radar which enables an aeroplane to find its destination from thousands of kilometres away can be called the same.

Some people in INRA (French National Institute for Agricultural Research) who are dogged in their criticism despite the enormous damage and debts they continue to inflict on both human beings and the earth, nowadays call it 'obscurantist' without wishing to understand that their instruments simply cannot measure these energy phenomena – which they therefore refuse to believe exist despite the convincing qualitative results.

The effects of biodynamics derive from real laws, just as much as the law Newton discovered when watching his apple fall. It is a shame, in fact, that people have focused on this law of gravity so exclusively, for Newton also spoke of opposing principles — of solar laws which must be perceived in a different way than by instruments geared solely to the world of matter. And this is something which is once more coming to light thanks to certain physicists, sometimes much scorned by their colleagues, who discover that behind the physical world there is another, which is wholly overlooked. The void is not the void, they say, but is full of other forces. Science is taking a great step forward here.

For us viticulturists and for all who are passionate about wine, what counts above all are the results; and as far as I am aware no viticulturist using conventional agriculture can, without artificial aids and technologies, equal the quality obtained by biodynamic methods, this agriculture of the future, nor even approach the originality of these wines when things are properly managed.

We have spoken of frequencies, of a world of energies underlying and sustaining life, of archetypal forces. All these little understood words seem a little primitive at the first reading. What is biodynamics really? What are the actual measures we use for our vines? How is it different from other methods of cultivation? It is time to get to grips with this subject.

4

Biodynamics in Viticulture

'Bio' means life; and 'dynamic', or 'dynamism' is an enhancement, an acceleration or also a stimulation of life. How does one dynamise life? It's very simple really. Let us say first of all that these processes already exist in nature, partially at least. Everyone knows, for example, that a mineral water, before being immobilized in a bottle, is much more biologically active and dynamic because of the movements to which it has been subject while circulating underground. One can also say that rainwater, which everyone knows is much better for plant growth than tap water, has been dynamised by the atmosphere.

Biodynamic agriculture began in 1924 in Germany, at the estate of Count and Countess Keyserlingk in Koberwitz, when Rudolf Steiner decided to give some very precise suggestions to improve the health of plants, their taste and their nutritional qualities. He gave advice for developing some specific natural preparations to enhance life processes, which plants need to express themselves fully. To do this he first selected some medicinal plants.

These were camomile, yarrow, nettle, oak bark, dandelion and valerian. Then, for some of these, he identified corresponding animal organs, with which they create a synergy.

He advised that most plants should be inserted into these animal organs for a certain period to reinforce their effects and, usually in winter – though in summer in one case – should be buried in the ground under fairly specific conditions, and be dug up again in spring.

Let us explain this in very clear terms to avoid the accusation of sorcery by our detractors – who are becoming ever more virulently opposed to these methods in the face of the qualitative success of biodynamic viticulture in increasing numbers of countries. Let us take a specific example: everyone knows that camomile has a connection with or particular effect on the digestion, and more specifically on the intestines. We also know that animals are more evolved and therefore higher than plants. Plants are wholly subject to the living organism surrounding them, composed of the earth, the sun, the climate etc., which they are wholly dependent on. The animal, on the other hand, internalizes the world in different organs: respiratory, digestive, cerebral etc., which give it a certain autonomy that allows it to drink, eat or sleep where it wants. Certain plants – the orchids in particular – take on slightly animal characteristics, those of insects for example, revealing perhaps the first tentative step towards developing this superior state.

To understand this idea better one needs to read the books by Pelikan,* referred to previously, on medicinal plants. It is

* Wilhelm Pelikan, *Healing Plants* (op. cit.).

always the case that this superior level of the animal world has powerful effects on plant growth. Everyone knows of course that animal manure is best for promoting plant growth. And what is this manure? Simply vegetable matter that has passed through an animal's digestive system. Except of course when crazy people, unable to distinguish the qualitative difference between a vegetable and animal protein, advise feeding cows with meat, which can make them go mad ('mad cow disease'). One can say, therefore, that manure is vegetable matter impregnated with an animal's metabolic forces. We all know, as well, that medicine often has recourse to remedies derived from the animal kingdom. These explanations – which are given here in very simplified form – can help us nevertheless to better understand the synergy that can exist between an animal organ and a plant, and provide the basis for developing certain natural preparations advised by Rudolf Steiner. I say 'very simplified' since the choice of plants, animal organs and animals involves profound understanding of archetypal life forces which are concentrated in each one of these preparations.

Ultimately, by enclosing camomile in an intestine, its properties will be reinforced or enhanced. So now all that remains is to choose the animal which has attained the greatest development of its digestive system, or which is the biggest ruminant in Europe. This is the cow, of course, which many ancient civilizations thought of as sacred, something also reflected in Christianity (the ox and ass in the stable). So one takes a cow's intestine and stuffs it with camomile, and buries it in winter. When spring comes one digs up this preparation again and adds very small quantities of it to a heap of manure or to a small pile of dung which is subsequently dynamised in water and sprayed on the soil at particular times. This is the principle. Enclosing the plant in an organ thus serves to enhance or activate a specific process. Certain plants are used without the aid of an animal organ (nettle and valerian), while others are inserted into other organs. The organ chosen for yarrow is the bladder of the deer, an animal figuring widely in symbolic or allgeorical texts, whose antlers give it immense sensitivity. For the dandelion one uses the cow's mesentery, the fine, silica-rich interior wall enclosing the cow's intestines. Oak bark is inserted into the vessel of a domestic animal's skull. Here we see the vegetable calcium of oak bark (77% calcium content) placed in synergy with the calcium in the skull of an animal.

All this is easily understood. There are much more profound explanations, though these too are no doubt incomplete, but there is no space to go further into this here. The sole aim of this book is to help wine lovers to understand why biodynamics has real effects which improve taste, longevity etc. When we speak of the specificity of each organ and of each animal used for these preparations, and include the forces which underlie life, everything becomes much more complex. Many justified questions cannot be discussed here, for instance the effect of burying the preparations in winter or summer, of burying them deep or closer to the surface, in a very dry or damp soil, in fertile or muddy ground. Why a cow and not an ox, a deer rather than a pig? Let us say, simply, that nothing is left to chance and that every detail has its importance for achieving precise effects. Those who wish to explore this approach further are referred to the Bibliography.

Thus the biodynamic preparations enable us to use the synergies available in nature, and all we need to do is know how to use them ...

We still need to mention one, very precious, organ which our detractors try to ridicule: the cow's horn, used for two preparations.

This organ is of immense importance for the cow. In stark contrast to the deer's antlers which act like antennae, the horn and hoof serve first and foremost, according to Steiner, to retain in the cow's interior the currents of forces which would otherwise seek to escape. Thus the horn and the hoof act as a kind of internal reflector. Outwardly it participates in the connection which the animal has with solar forces of ascension, something one can also see in ancient Egyptian depictions of the goddess Hathor (who brings the heavenly gift of wine to the earth) with the head of a cow and a solar disc situated between her horns. The horn enables the cow to bear its heavy head with ease and grace. Its horns are permeated with a specific process of great interest to viticulturists who are continually seeking to improve the taste of their wine. It is true, of course, that agricultural schools nowadays advise de-horning cows, a widespread practice which people carry out without awareness of its significance. What use are these horns, they ask.

In ancient times the horn was viewed as the source of richness and abundance. Old paintings depict the 'cornucopia' from which abundance, pieces of gold or other precious objects pour forth, but today few understand this symbol nor the forces it represents. In Denmark and Georgia they still sell horns inlaid with silver for drinking wine or water – the last vestige of past times when, to announce that it was time to eat, people still used the phrase 'The water is horned'. Yes, indeed, water was poured into a horn which instilled into it the frequencies the horn retains for several years after its removal, giving the water health-giving properties.

In the case of biodynamic preparations one fills the horns with cow dung and buries them in the winter in a carefully chosen place. If, by way of experiment, one buries next to such horns the same dung in a little terracotta pot one finds, on digging both up again in spring, that the dung in the horn contains about 70 times more bacteriological activity. Yet again we discover that a proper understanding of the life that surrounds us can invoke powerful forces which will benefit our plants. Only the contents of one or two horns are used per hectare, which may come to 100 or 150 grams of dung. How does one spread such little quantities over a whole hectare? It is very simple. Without going into every detail, basically we dynamise this dung in 60 or 70 litres of lukewarm water. How? By creating a vortex or spiralling eddy in a container of the mixture, either by using a long, suspended stick if one does it by hand, or by using a dynamising machine. In less than a minute, when this vortex reaches almost to the bottom of the container, one reverses it as quickly as possible, then continues the process (see Plate 8).

We can say, quite simply, that this strong agitation enables the properties of the horned dung to enter the water mixture that is subsequently sprayed on the soil. We can also say that the latent forces underlying life often manifest in physical matter in the form of spirals. One can see this in the petals of the rose, a wonderful, opening spiral formation, in the arrangement of seeds in a sunflower, in the position of shoots around the stem of certain plants including the rose, and also to some extent in the tufts of animal fur or the hairs on a human head. This form is engraved on some menhirs, manifests of course in cyclones, and on shells etc., and can be found everywhere around us if we are attentive to it. (See over and Plates 9, 10 and 11.)

Studies are currently being carried out on spirals by the CNRS (French National Council for Scientific Research). The book by Theodor Schwenk, *Sensitive Chaos*, shows many examples and illustrations of this. What is the significance of this spiral form? In simple terms, a macrocosm that becomes a microcosm; a periphery that becomes a centre; a journey

from something dispersed and intangible to the condensation point of matter.

The preparation made by these means is sprayed on the soil in the evening as the sinking sun draws the atmosphere towards the earth, condensing it into dew.

To understand how it works we just need to realize that each drop of this preparation is a vector or mediator of microbial life that can activate our soil and help it to develop the mycorhiza we mentioned earlier. You will recall that the more intense microbial life is, the better vine roots can seize hold through them of all geological aspects of the soil. Thus we introduce into the soil life processes in the form of micro-organisms of all kinds which have been activated by passing through a horn. Basically the horn acts as a nursery that cultivates the life of micro-organisms in the dung we put into it. Each one is the mediator of, often different, information. Then, through dynamisation, one inseminates the soil with all these various processes. Thus we imbue the soil with life processes which can only develop if the ground is 'receptive' or, if you like, where there is a welcoming milieu. For this to work it is necessary for the soil to be free of these terrible poisons which are increasingly injuring human health but whose use is still advised in agriculture in the form of herbicides and chemical treatments. One cannot engender a life process on the one hand, and on the other initiate a death process and think this will achieve something! We need to make a choice for one or the other approach, and not mix the two.

The highly fertilizing property of horns has been known since the beginning of time. They are sold in the form of bonemeal or powder by almost all agricultural associations. Let me mention in passing that the compulsory treatment of this product, recently introduced because of a continued failure to understand mad cow syndrome, has rendered it much less effective. It is interesting to note that in France, whenever a natural product has a significant effect, a pretext is found — always in the name of people's supposed welfare — to diminish its qualities. We have seen the same thing recently in relation to homeopathic substances used since the dawn of time, which are still accepted in other countries.

Ultimately the sole difference, though an important one, between ground horns and this biodynamic preparation is that in biodynamics we use the horn as a container for the dung, to concentrate its forces, rather than as matter itself. The dung placed in the horn is impregnated during the winter with forces or dynamisms active both in the horn and the earth, which enable the horn to be preserved for three to four years.

The horn serves to develop another preparation too. We fill it with quartz instead of dung – that is, silica in the form of very fine powder. Our earth contains this in great quantities and Steiner tells us that it plays an important role in maintaining equilibrium in nature, even if it appears to be inert. It acts as link or medium, a sort of receptive antenna, to certain forces which radiate from the solar system.

To make this preparation one fills the horn with quartz powder and buries it in the ground during summer. This powder, subsequently removed from the horn again, is imbued with very particular energies, frequencies and information. The word 'information' may alarm some people, and yet everyone knows that quartz or silica is used in information technology as a medium of information, or alternatively can be 'charged' to make our watches or other equipment function. In our particular case the charge or the information is given by nature via the horn and the earth in which it is buried, this time during summer. This is very simple isn't it? To use this preparation we take infinitesimal quantities of a few grams per hectare. In speaking of frequencies weight has no significance – this would make no sense. In biodynamics we are not dealing with quantities but, as we have seen, with energies. You are not charged for your mobile phone use by the weight of its waves – say 2 grams for Paris and 100 grams for New York! You do not receive your TV programmes by weight, but nevertheless you see very definite visual effects. When you turn the button on your radio you locate different programmes by turning to different frequencies — and all of this seems normal because you are used to it. But it is no less true to say that the descent of life to earth, whose material effects become visible in spring, obeys somewhat similar laws. This means that trying to understand the life of a plant by focusing exclusively on the plant itself, as modern science too often does, is as useless as looking for the presenter of a TV programme inside the television itself. The plant and the seed are but a receiver, linked to a vast system we need to understand if we are going to make use of it. We have been told that genes are merely intermediaries which obey the orders they receive. Biodynamic preparations function somewhat like transmitters, mobilizing and activating precise energies and processes which plants nowadays receive to a much lesser extent due both to the disruption people have caused in the soil and also in the atmosphere in the form of radio waves etc. Until now people have regarded the atmosphere as an energy dustbin into which one can dump whatever frequencies one likes, high or low, without even suspecting that this has direct effects on life. No serious funding is made available for conclusions which might have an anti-commercial impact, and even if it was, very well-organized lobbies would ensure that research does not go down a path that could lead to 'wrong conclusions'. But we have a responsibility to future generations, and it is high time we became aware of the effects of our actions, and found the courage to put long-term health before short-term profit.

To recap, then, each biodynamic preparation is the bearer of a specific process at the energy level. It acts somewhat like a sensor or vector. The brilliant thing about biodynamic agriculture is that it mediates information to and from this invisible but very real system of energies which is activated to give life to the earth. It stimulates and directs it. It acts at a stage before life becomes, or is imprisoned in, matter. All this will come to seem self-evident in a few decades.

Thus invisible energy information is mediated by the quartz via the horn and the summer earth. Then we put a few grams of the silica into water and dynamise it for an hour, then spray it in the morning on the leaves rather than the earth itself, for otherwise it will not have the desired effect. This needs to happen early in the morning because this is the moment when the rising sun acts like the spring season, drawing sap upwards and connecting the plant to upper worlds. What are we really doing when we use this prepara-tion? We are, in fact, using the quartz to draw in the air's luminosity. In today's sadly mundane terms we might say that we are 'passing light information' and thus activating photosynthesis. Also, if the moment is well-chosen, this strengthens a connection with the forces that give rise to taste. The preparation is extremely powerful. It can also help the vine to exhale excess water or act as anti-fungal treatment. Without entering into all the details, the main thing to remember is that it needs to be used with care and caution since today's atmosphere is no longer the same as it was in

1924 when Steiner first gave his indications. Today's atmosphere is less alive. Steiner spoke of the atmosphere as the place where cosmic laws tune themselves to earthly laws — something which is less effective nowadays. If the weather is too dry or hot, this treatment should not be given.*

You now have enough insight into biodynamics to understand it in principle, and to grasp how it acts or, if you prefer, how it connects the vine to processes working in nature since time immemorial. Biodynamics seeks only to activate. It does not set up frequency fields in the atmosphere to use them subsequently, as mobile phones do, but it makes use of what nature has already put in place to generate life on earth and merely activates and enhances this.

To sum up, then, very small quantities of plant-based preparations are placed into a manure heap or into a few kilos of dung, and act as catalysts for processes which the plant depends on to express itself fully in the physical realm: processes of potassium, calcium, iron, silica, phosphorus; and also of fruiting — in other words, very briefly, of what halts the growth of leaves and branches and enables fruit to develop. One can even understand these preparations by saying that by inserting them into a manure heap they will act a little like the working of organs in an animal, each one having a very precise role to play. Specifically, via micro-

---

* See Nicholas Joly, *Wine from Sky to Earth* (Acres U.S.A., Texas), which gives more detailed advice for practising farmers and viticulturists.

fauna that are different and very particular in each case, they will reinforce very precise functions in the soil and the plant. If they have been inserted into manure this will be spread in the autumn, preferably digging it in to the soil. If, instead, they are inserted into small quantities of dung, this will be dynamised and then applied to the soil. The autumn is the ideal moment for these tasks, for then the sun that has become ascendant in the southern hemisphere draws everything downwards in the northern hemisphere, and the soil becomes ready to 'receive' or welcome to its bosom the impulses one desires to give it.* Later, in the midst of winter, when cold reigns, the earth crystallizes and, through its crystals, hearkens to a more distant world. We might say that this is the time when the earth, via its crystals, is 'inspired' by the solar and stellar system – an inspiration which will come to full creative expression as spring returns and plants begin to reach up again to their macrocosmic source, producing at the same time sustenance for animals and human beings. Mother earth is continually inspired by the solar and stellar system. During winter she is less active, although not so much resting as receiving influences. This winter moment is very precious for all that occurs beyond the physical plane seemingly immersed in sleep. This is the moment when life, unleashed to some extent from its connection with matter, is present only in the form of energy. Steiner tells us that this is

----

* In the southern hemisphere, of course, this applies in reverse.

the time of year when we can inwardly hearken to our fields and our vines, harmonizing them through our thoughts alone. This was very common in the past, when farmers would 'keep the midnight watch' or gather at one neighbour's house or another in turn, to reflect, listen, think and understand things better than the intellect alone allowed. If we deepen these suggestions of a somewhat meditative nature, we can discover here a rich realm of almost untapped possibilities which we can try to develop if we so wish. So-called 'green fingers' are an unconscious version of this faculty. By reflecting in this way the human being can no doubt try to consciously reacquire such capacities.

The two preparations placed in cow horns have functions that are quite distinct from the other preparations. The one made with dung acts like a growth vector in the soil, mobilizing the life of the soil and connecting it to the vine's roots through an intense microbial life. Thus it helps recreate the vine's physical body, of which, after pruning, there is nothing left but the stock and a few shoots and buds from the previous year. At the beginning of spring, therefore, we need to help the vine to develop as the buds are about to open.

The quartz-based preparation acts via the light and thus has *different effects according to the season when it is used*. The vine, after all, does different things in spring and autumn. This preparation, one can say, accompanies the vine in its daily task. In spring, when the vine is in full growth and creating matter to give birth to its shoots, tendrils and leaves, its help is from above as it were, that is to say through the leaves via photosynthesis. Applied several weeks after the summer solstice, when the days begin to grow shorter again, at the moment when the vine is fully mobilized to mature its grapes, the preparation helps these to form their sugars and tastes via an increased influx of air-borne luminosity. It is this warmth of luminosity, carried on the air, which mediates forces of the solar world that generate taste, scent and aroma.

I trust that it is becoming clear that it is not enough just to 'practise' a biodynamic method in order to obtain a good wine but we also need to try to fully understand how it works. Our understanding of the preparations, of our terrain, the vitality of the vines, the grape variety, the growth forces in the soil, the climatic profile of the year, all help the viticulturist to take the decisions he needs to. Thus one can use both of the preparations made in the horn to achieve a vine that is either more or less present on the physical plane, or, if you like, more or less active in its Dionysian combativeness. At one extreme we can have a large vine with lustrous leaves whose forces of fruiting and taste will be lessened by this exuberance of foliage. At the other extreme we can have a smaller vine with thinner branches, but whose wine will reveal strength and beauty. Exuberance and fruit formation are somewhat opposed. One frequently sees a tendency to one or other of these two extremes.

Biodynamics is the first type of agriculture, at least for several centuries, to give back to cultivators the possibility of affecting plant behaviour on a plane other than the physical – which only allows it limited potential for diversity. This agriculture involves a labour that is almost artistic when we start to ask ourselves how to help a vine best express itself. The possible choices are very diverse. One can reinforce the vine's connections to particular functions to which, at present, it has only poor access. Take the silica process for example – why increase or reduce this? Simply, first of all, because the earth of today is no longer what it was in former times. The earth also grows older, and no longer has such a powerful capacity for growth as it had a few millennia ago, when it developed immense trees – just look at the thickness of the coal strata – or enormous animals. Finally, and above all, our progress in the physical, material realm has often been disastrous for the realm of energies. This aspect is only just starting to become the subject of research but, as I have said several times elsewhere – and without any political emphasis, since ecology really should not be politicized – powerful vested interests try to silence such studies for as long as possible.

The silver lining to the cloud, and there always is one, is that all this gives viticulturists and genuine cultivators the chance to work qualitatively in a way that is increasingly recognized and appreciated by consumers throughout the world. By using biodynamics one can, in the same vineyard, produce a wine that is more or less luminous, more or less earthy, more or less floral, etc. And isn't it also to some extent up to the winegrower, whose situation compared to farmers has been somewhat privileged over the past two decades, to show that all these subtleties worthy of securing an AOC designation can likewise be found in certain milk products, vegetables or fruits? This would encourage consumers to use their purchasing power to make careful choices about the foods they buy, full of original, authentic tastes that earth forces give when one knows how to invoke them. The viticulturist would be able to demonstrate a certain creativity if he wishes, and engage in other actions, with no need to make a secret of them. For example, in adverse climatic conditions, one can apply herbal teas to vines to help them accomplish their task. The vine is a living being. People believe that it fulfils its nature automatically, but this is far from true. Creating sugar in a grape is laborious work, for example. It is possible to use a rose hip tea (fruit of the sweet briar) to stimulate the formation of sugars a few weeks prior to harvest.

One can protect the vine from the impact of sunshine rendered more aggressive by our irresponsible acts by treating it with a tea prepared from seaweed. Such actions do not violate the vine as technology does. Instead of treating it by purely physical means these teas call forth the vine's own reactions of sympathy and antipathy.

One can also ask which animal is most appropriate to our land, as this too will play something like the role of an organ in the 'living organism' which an agricultural entity represents. Each animal, very directly through its dung, will have a different, tangible effect on the taste of a wine. Each animal is subject in different ways to the four states of matter, and through its dominating principle will affect the roots, the leaves, flowers or fruits. The horse gives a better taste to the wine than the pig, for example.

One of the important things which Steiner states about biodynamic agriculture (and anthroposophic medicine) is that it does not 'combat' a disease but promotes an equilibrium, and by this means renders the carriers of disease far less potent. This holistic notion of the agricultural organism is an important one. Thus it may be a very good idea to sacrifice a little of our AOC terroir to leave a field, a wood, fallow ground or a tree at the very least! Every aspect of life, and therefore every species of plant or animal, will attract a different fauna of birds, insects and microbes, etc. which will influence the life of our soils and the mycorhiza of which the vine has such need to unfold the full distinction of its AOC. Every intervention that accords with the overall harmony of the farm or vineyard will not only limit the influx of diseases but will also reinforce the incredibly complex system which gives rise to a wine's beauty, aromas, colours and health-giving properties.

Would there be any danger of avian flu if birds had not been raised in tightly packed battery cages? Has a single state veterinarian had the courage to say so? And if he were to do this, wouldn't he lose his job? Teaching today in the realm of animal health has sunk to the depths of materialism and intellectual aridity. Think of all those young cows gorged on silage — to produce high milk yields — which have to be killed before the age of seven in order to hide their cirrhosis, which would render them unsellable. Think of all the animal proteins which farmers continue to feed them, heating them to 600° to prevent cows — temporarily at least — from passing on mad cow disease. Think of the huge reluctance to understand that animal and vegetable protein are qualitatively different, and that the cow is not a carnivore. Think of sheep scrapie and swine fever. The list is long and costly, very costly. Should such costs, at least, not motivate us to change our approach?

We are plunged so deep in error that we have the right, as taxpayers, to ask this question. Do we have before us a veterinary service which opposes irresponsible animal rearing practices, or proof of complicity in error? It is due only to over-use of antibiotics that these almost barbarian agricultural acts have not yet manifested in innumerable consequences for the human being. Veterinary teaching is so narrow that the members of this profession — although fortunately there are always exceptions — sometimes seem like unwitting torturers who focus exclusively on treating symptoms with all sorts of medicines or vaccines with serious secondary effects, without ever trying to address the cause. Soon, when the whole life system has been destroyed, they will no doubt make out that it is only due to them that we are still alive! These are the same people who use a dangerous, internal insecticide treatment just to treat cattle grubs – a simple gadfly that pierces the skin – which you then eat in your meat without realizing it. The unbelievable pretext for this treatment is that these insect bites reduce the value of the hide. In this same case, though, thanks to the courageous intervention of an open-minded minister in the agriculture department, organic farmers have obtained the right to avoid this absurd law, indirectly issued by powerful lobby groups.

The new toy astutely slipped into the hands of these veterinary services is the electronic chip implanted in animals, which imposes on them a rhythm which isn't their own, of course, and which thus distances them from their own rhythmic system, the very core of their health. The commercial argument behind this measure, which is still presented as progress, is that it prevents animals being stolen. The truth is that if they are, it is easy to detect this chip and remove it. Examples of such aberrant measures are too numerous to ignore. The 'Paris Appeal', a petition submitted to the public services by high-profile oncologists – alarmed by the growing number of children admitted for treatment – and by other well-known individuals, demonstrates a just and effective means for limiting all these abuses.

The same problems rear their heads in viticulture, agriculture and animal rearing: Should one treat the cause or the effect? What is health? In choosing always only to act in response to the effects of absurd practices we will never achieve much progress, that is, grow health-giving foods. Is it necessary to initiate legal proceedings in order to show that the avian flu virus, which has made vast profits for vaccine producers, has existed for a long time, and that birds have carried this virus for decades, only rarely dying from it? It only becomes dangerous, in fact, when rearing conditions are so ridiculous.

Forgive me for this digression from the subject of wine; but to try to avoid such dramas continuing and multiplying with exponential speed, the consumer needs to be warned. One can even regard it as a civic duty to do so. After all, the consumer rules at the end of the day. It is thus right to tell him the full truth. If he changes his purchasing habits the strategies and tricks of big vested interests will crumble in a second.

Finally we need to look at a system to which we have referred above on several occasions, one which brings life and health: I mean the solar system. What does it mean for the earth? Why does the earth belong to a solar system? What would it be without it?

5

The Solar and Stellar System, and its Effects on the Earth

In our daily life we are more aware of our connection with the sun than with the integral totality of a solar system in which all the planets and the earth are involved. This awareness of the sun develops most in its absence which we sense, quickly enough, as a cruel lack, whose return rapidly gives us back a feeling of comfort and even indolence. Apart from the sun we are often also attentive to the moon which we admire when it is magnificently full. This is often the extent of many people's awareness of the solar system. The moment we speak of a 'system' in fact, we need to understand that all these constituents mutually interact – as in a living organism in which each organ contributes in its own way, and with its own inherent characteristics, to a global whole which is greater than the sum of its parts. It is thus through a kind of synergy that each of the constituents of the solar system, including the planets, affect the earth, and that the earth, in turn, acts upon this system. This knowledge is something we need to rediscover, and it is encouraging to find that such work is already underway.

To reassure our Cartesians, though, let us ask ourselves

first how and by what means such effects might actually exert an influence on the earth. Our first impulse is probably to say that something located millions of kilometres away cannot really affect our physical environment or ourselves in any tangible way. And this is the nub of the problem, where we find ourselves trapped by the limits of the physical, sensory world. Throughout this book I have reiterated that the forces of life do not belong to matter itself but to a complex and organized world of energies, made of wavelengths of all kinds which certain scientists are trying to identify. Isn't it by means of this same world of energies that people can send orders from the earth to a robot standing on Mars which, a few seconds later, carries them out? Likewise, we have already seen that the sun acts upon our earth by means of diverse wavelengths. Aren't we in fact completely connected to it via an overall plane of energies? So why should we deny a similar connection to other parts of the solar system, or to the more distant stellar system called the zodiac? Let us recall once again that our senses only perceive a small part of all that exists.

We also need to be aware that, thanks to certain energy forces, atoms cohere together and matter becomes accessible to our senses, despite the fact that it remains composed of a world of vibrations whose continual movement we do not perceive. The whole earth, right into its smallest corners, is continually bombarded by all sorts of frequencies and cosmic wavelengths whose origin we are unaware of. We know of their existence but not yet their meaning. A big international funding programme is even constructing ultra-powerful antennae and satellite dishes to try to decipher the language or coherence of these frequencies. Our sole error is to impose on them our own, very terrestrial interpretation.

When we approach life in a different way than via infinitely small atoms we enter instead into a quite different kind of understanding, which we can summarize as follows:

Everything that lives is sustained by different rhythms, frequencies, and wavelengths. Physical death can be seen as just the absence of certain rhythms. Each planet, or more precisely each planetary sphere — since each physical planet can be seen as the focus of a sphere of activity rather than its sole, active element — has its own characteristic 'energy language'. The closer we approach to the sun, the more the frequencies mix and interpenetrate which are linked to the concentric circles that the planets and the earth describe around the solar star. I am not going to try to explain here the incredibly creative complexity of this system in its effects on the earth. Steiner, Elisabeth Vreede, Rudolf Hauschka and many others have all written volumes on this subject which one can study and gradually assimilate. Here I just want to stress, firstly, that before becoming physical all that composes life is in the form of energy information to which matter obediently responds. Matter is never the mould, only the content of the mould, something that is increasingly being understood. Recently researchers have discovered a way of charting the energy maps of each human illness and have recorded them as part of a promising project which may open the doors to very economical preventive methods. Diagnosis of a precise field of resonance, which creates the pre-conditions for a physical illness to manifest, will enable us to act before the latter occurs. If we discover these frequency anomalies, or this resonance map of an illness, we will know that the danger of this illness appearing is great. This approach can help us understand that energy information or a resonance field will sooner or later manifest physically. To put this in simple terms we can say that the whole solar and stellar system forms a totality of thousands of resonance maps which facilitate permanent dialogue between the earth and the other members of this system. Ultimately all this is just information which will eventually take form in matter in some way.

At the physical level the earth is composed of minerals, plants, animals and human beings, all of which are accessible to our senses. But let us not forget that these physical mani-festations are composed of particles that are assembled and densified by specific informational forces.

What is it that gathers two hydrogen atoms with one oxy-gen atom so as to produce water? This is the important question. Water is not just composed of two molecules of hydrogen and one of oxygen as we are taught (so that we can become an agricultural engineer or a vet kow-towing before the might of the chemicals industry). *Besides its constituent atoms water is also the force which gathers them together.* Without this there would be no water! We can demonstrate this in a more down-to-earth example: would you prefer to eat a cake or its separate constituents? A chef or cook is needed to gather the ingredients in a creative act, to produce a successful dish. One would not dismiss the work of the cook, but praise him as the originator of the cake. So why should we hide acknowledgement of the active or formative forces as they are known in biodynamics? Are we worried that these discoveries will undermine the whole gigantic market in artificials? What do these forces do which are used by bio-dynamics, homeopathy, music therapy and many other methods that go back to primordial times, whose beneficial effects are becoming ever more widely recognized? They connect matter with the resonance of its originating formative plane.

So how do we use these formative forces? This is also something that Rudolf Steiner dealt with in his Agricultural Course, and in many other works which relate to the sources of life. Life on earth is nothing but a dialogue between visible and an invisible world; an invisible, formative world and a world that is formed and is accessible to our physical senses. This interaction occurs through continuous 'incarnation' or physical embodiment of centripetal forces, and ascent or disembodiment of centrifugal forces. When a plant, after forming its stem and blossom, arrives at the pollen-forming stage, it has almost attained a stage of non-matter largely emancipated from gravity. This allows pollen to fly up into the air to a height of several thousand metres. Annuals thus complete their cycle by being partly dematerialized, firstly, and then contracted to an extreme in the seed. Thus in autumn one sees separate the forces which spring had united. All around us centrifugal forces ceaselessly interpenetrate with centripetal ones. Aromas, tastes and colours can only descend to the physical plane when forces are reversed, that is to say when a process of growth has come to a halt. Without this, fruit cannot form properly, something aided and supported by one of the biodynamic preparations. Of course these two stages are not totally separate: at a certain moment they interpenetrate. But we cannot achieve a fine taste when growth has been over-forced, something which ultimately opposes the process of latent contraction underlying fruiting.

It is for this reason that the vine needs to be in something of a combat situation, so that its growth is reined in to produce a good wine. The fruiting forces descend more easily where growth is weaker. Thus we cannot properly understand how life manifests on earth without always trying to take account of these two opposing forces. In the same way each planet has a current which approaches matter and aids the plant's physical incarnation; and another, opposite current which first halts its growth and then encourages the process of dematerialization. The sun is also sensitive to these two aspects of life which one can call springlike and autumnal, even though they do not always adhere to the seasonal calendar. One can even say that it is the sun that activates these. Let us never forget, though, that the sun is less an agent than a coordinator.

Let us recall, also, that two biodynamic preparations support these two solar aspects. On the one hand the horn dung which mobilizes matter in the plant, and on the other the horn silica which forms and sculpts this matter. Every other biodynamic preparation – based on camomile, yarrow, nettle, oak bark, dandelion and valerian – acts as a connection to the archetypal forces of the five planets and the moon. Biodynamics is just an enhancement of the solar system's manifestations on the earth, at a time when, due to our grave lack of understanding, its influences have been drastically weakened by the energy dustbin we are making of our atmosphere. Above all, as Steiner impresses on us, the atmosphere is the place of interaction between earthly and cosmic laws, without which the earth would be a corpse. Energy pollution of the atmosphere (physical pollution is actually less grave) weakens the life forces which sustain the earth and thus many of those which also sustain the human being. This is why biodynamics has become so important: it responds at the energy level to an alarming imbalance. It reconnects the earth to its sources. This is also how we can understand its effect on radioactivity, to which it represents an opposite pole. In Poland, at the time of Chernobyl, on a biodynamic commune, scientists measured only 1/10th of the radioactivity which was present elsewhere. Biodynamics helps forces descend and incarnate whereas radioactivity is escaping, de-materializing life. Two hundred years ago bio-dynamics would probably have had less relevance. Today it has become essential, firstly in relation to taste, to wine and food quality, but also in relation to the life which the earth needs to maintain its equilibrium. The climate, after all, is composed of nothing but balances and harmonies. The troubles which plague it cannot be ascribed to warming alone.

So we can say that the solar and stellar system emits forces which form and sculpt matter, or which weave its threads together. According to the season it has a densifying or dis-sipating effect. In delivering energy from the prison of matter, we open a door to the pure forces of life. This is what also distinguishes biodynamics from homeopathy. Biodynamics, unlike homeopathy, draws on and reinforces the archetypal forces of the solar system which a plant needs. These two opposing but also complementary levels, of the tangible and intangible, are jointly active all around us. *Both are necessary for our understanding of life on earth. The one should not conceal the other.*

Thus we should regard the solar system as an 'information' system whose task is to generate on earth organisms which conserve the forces of life while also coming to physical manifestation. When these life forces are extinguished by matter's density they can no longer survive as they no longer penetrate matter sufficiently. This is what we call death. This just means a departure of life from the physical plane. The energy plane cannot die, but only transform. This is what Goethe meant when he said that nature invented death to recreate life:

> As long as you have not grasped
> Life issuing forth from death
> You're but a troubled guest
> Upon the shrouded earth.

The solar system is composed, as we know, of the five planets, the moon our satellite, and the sun which acts rather like the conductor of an orchestra. The moon's reflective action is somewhat like an intermediary between the earth and the solar system.

It is important to understand the moon better: for example, breeding either at full or new moon helps determine the sex of an animal. Having a female covered by a male on the day of either the full or new moon gives an 80 percent likelihood that, respectively, a male or female offspring will be born. Biodynamic breeders actually already know something about this.

The moon acts as an intermediary between the solar system and the earth, exerting an important effect on plant growth. From new moon towards full moon its forces draw plants upwards. From full moon to new moon, in contrast, forces are progressively orientated earthwards, and thus stimulate root growth.

We can now present the solar system as a living organism and not as an engine in which all the parts just keep repeating the same movements continuously, for in life nothing repeats exactly in the same way. The revolutions of the planets, their years if you like, always vary a little. That of Mercury, the most irregular, can vary by eight days. The sun itself is never exactly at the centre of the more or less elliptical orbits that the planets describe around it. Their rotational planes in relation to the sun can also reveal differences, as can their speed of orbit. All this really testifies to a living organism. This collective dance of the earth and the planets around the sun — a little like the electrons compelled to encircle an atom — is full of irregularities and thus, as we will see, often provides a wealth of opportunities for viticulturists or farmers who know how to perceive and use it. All these irregularities also help us to understand that each day has a unique, unrepeatable aspect, which hopefully renders us more attentive to its particular characteristics.

There are two simple, basic rules for making use of this knowledge. These draw on the four states of matter which we mentioned at the beginning. Firstly we can say that the planetary or stellar impulses express themselves in four principle ways, linked to these four states of matter: that of fruiting (heat impulse), blossoming (light impulse), leaf growth (water impulse) and finally root growth (earth impulse). The second rule is that, according to the positions of the planets in relation to the earth, and in relation to the stellar constellations present behind them as they orbit the sun, these different influences act in a more or less pronounced and harmonious way. In specific instances, such as an eclipse, lunar or planetary nodes (when planets cross the sun's plane), lunar apogee or perigee positions (when the moon is furthest from or nearest to the earth), these can have some very adverse effects.

Of course the whole earth is always subject to these influences, whether one studies them in chemistry, biology or biodynamics. But when agriculture has killed the majority of living agents such as a soil's micro-organisms, or has modified the growth of a plant through artificial interventions such as chemical fertilizers or dangerous systemic herbicides etc., the plant becomes less receptive, or not receptive at all, to these celestial influences. It is like someone falling ill and losing some of his capacity for communication. In consequence the plant becomes somewhat deaf to these invisible, qualitative planes of life, and this is why the resonance qualities of so much of our food are so poor for human nutrition – as quality tests, so-called sensitive crystallization, have shown. These tests enable us to observe a product's energy organization, and are done with copper chloride, as powder, mixed with the juice of any food. The liquid is placed on a piece of glass, and then in a controlled-humidity Petri box. As it dries up the product's life forces draw the powder in lines, producing a shape somewhat similar to frost flowers on a window. If the product is devoid of life forces no image will arise but merely a spot of dried-up powder. If it is alive, the resulting image can be analysed and the quality of the product determined by the pattern's regularity, peripheral structure and the precision at its centre.

Plate 12 demonstrates the crystallization of white compared with unrefined sugar. Over-refinement completely destroys life forces.

Plate 13 shows the crystallization of an organic strawberry, with no precise centre. This is probably not due to the cultivation method but to clone-based selection methods.

Plate 14 (bottom) indicates the poor crystallization image of a wine produced using artificial methods. The top image shows very good crystallization of white wine, showing excellent structure and detail, as well as a very precise centre. The middle picture is the same wine after passing under a barcode reader. Although this process lasts less than a second, one can clearly see that the image has changed. The pattern now shows distinct areas of weakness. So we can see that a barcode reader is not neutral in its effect on wine, interfering with the natural rhythms of which life is constituted.

Plate 15 illustrates the capacity of a biodynamic wine, which is full of life forces, to resist the forces of destruction at work in the process of oxidation. A bottle that was half-full is recorked but not placed in the fridge, then studied for 9 consecutive days. From the 7th day you can see clean filament patterning developing in the structure.

This demonstrates the fact that many biodynamic wines actually improve several days after they have been opened. Such tests are fine tools for showing the action of energy forces in the physical world, and the interference caused by many of our modern technologies. Of course, powerful lobby interests will oppose such knowledge. It is also interesting to know that the shell of an unboiled egg considerably reduces energy-wave pollution. (This explains why small quantities of crushed, uncooked eggshell — in a fine powder — are added to one of the biodynamic preparations advised by Maria Thun.)

The tests are also used on human blood, to ascertain the energy effects on it of any medicine prescribed. The images produced embody life forces. As we have already seen, what feeds us in our food are these forces rather than mere matter, and impoverished food will show little such life. In other words, an unsound agriculture isolates the plant from the vast context which gives it life, and, as we have already discussed, leads to the need to give it continuous artificial assistance. All living beings on earth, starting from the human being and his powers of cognition, but also all the plants, animals, insects, birds and micro-organisms of all kinds, even if they are minuscule, have a role to play in linking the earth to the macrocosm for which they act as intermediaries.

These insights can help each one of us to question conventional agricultural practices. When we speak of the macrocosm and its constituent aspects, we cannot do so without acknowledging the 40 years' work undertaken in

Germany by Maria Thun, with such rigour and courage. She has painstakingly measured each planetary and stellar influence on the plant world, and now regularly publishes a sowing and planting calendar as a guide for others.*

This agricultural *vade mecum* has opened up a whole field for further research. Isn't it interesting to observe, for instance, that several generations of wheat grains tuned fully to their proper planetary and stellar influences by a conscientious biodynamic practice, reduce wheat-related illnesses to almost nil. Thus wheat has recovered its former nutritious properties, and can once again nourish us fully. Such observations also apply to other plants. And all this knowledge is making consumers more aware of the economic interests underpinning the artificial interventions employed by conventional agriculture.

If we take account of the positions of the planets in relation to each other and to the stellar constellations, in this narrow band which includes the rotation of all the planets around the sun – which we call the zodiac in fact; and of the continuous, very rapid movement of the sun and our solar system towards the constellation of Vega; of the behaviour of the sun itself with its sudden eruptions; and of many other things as well, then we can see that each day really is unique and unrepeatable. This means in turn that all the influences

---

* Maria Thun, *Sowing and Planting Calendar* (Floris Books). See also *Gardening For Life* (Hawthorn Press, 1999) and *The Biodynamic Year* (Temple Lodge, 2007).

which reach us from the solar system via the living medium whose rediscovery began in 1831 with Faraday's radio waves – which he named 'the medium which links the emitting and the emitted principle' – are in permanent flux. Every angle of planets between each other and in relation to the earth has an energy effect differing according to mathematical laws.

There are kinds of 'information' which tend towards the harmonious formation of matter, and other kinds which oppose it. When we seek to generate a greater degree of life in a particular area we need to remember this. The ascending or

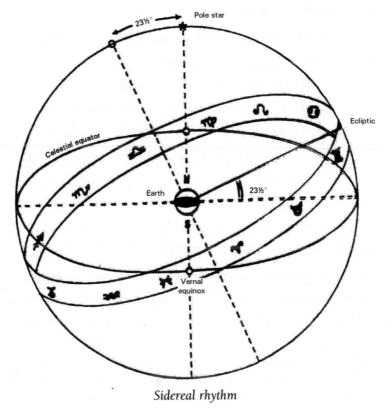

Sidereal rhythm

descending cycle of a planet does not generate the same conditions. We know this from observing the effects of the moon, but we also need to understand it at the level of all the planets, and discover health-giving forces there for every species of tree, each of which is always subject to a particular prevailing planetary influence. One sows a tree when its planet is in the ascendant, and transplants it when the planet is in the descendant. The principle is the same as the effect of the ascending moon on the plant's vegetative parts, and of the descending moon on a plant's roots. By transplanting at the right moment, you can tune a tree to its specific archetypal forces, which helps the roots to recover from the shock of transplanting, giving it much greater health and resistance to disease.* For distant planets like Saturn, it is sometimes worth waiting 15 years for the best moment to plant. I do not intend to give all the details of these procedures (see Bibliography for further reading) but to convey a vivid understanding of their rich diversity. The mercurial vine is best transplanted when Mercury is in the descendant.

All the particularities of the system in which we are embedded thus endow each day with a unique energy information profile, enabling us to ask how we can enhance certain effects, if we consider them desirable, in relation to our vines. All this knowledge produces results which each

---

* Maria Thun demonstrated this clearly several years ago in her study of pine plantations. Sixty years after planting, some trees were in a very poor condition while others close beside them were unaffected by diseases.

person can try out for himself and measure. There are innumerable examples. Where the laws which generate life can fully unfold, each plant reacts to the least influence with which one connects it: rather like pupils in a class who respond to the all the hints and suggestions of a teacher who knows how to present his knowledge in a way they can relate to. We are surrounded by examples which encourage us to take this kind of approach. It has already been scientifically demonstrated that certain people can speed up or slow down the growth of a plant through their very presence and way of thinking. Such heart forces should definitely not be overlooked. Crystallization techniques (see above) have shown that plants modify their behaviour 24 hours before a solar eclipse. We know that some animals sense the approach of an earthquake more than a day before it happens. We also know the reality of the so-called 'placebo' effect on human beings — which ultimately is information we unconsciously give ourselves. This new path of research is currently being pursued further by certain scientists who not only study this system of energies but are also starting to use its potential effects. These discoveries can lead to huge progress or problems, depending on the conscience of those who apply them. And here lies the nub of the problem. Are we ready for this kind of knowledge? Here's one example: intensive pig farming creates enormous problems of smell and pollution for several kilometres around. By giving each animal 2 grams of quartz per day that has been treated with certain alpine plants, the dung becomes normal again, and the animals' hides regain their glossiness. But do we have the right to make pigs believe they are in a mountain environment when in fact they are reared in an animal concentration camp? In other words, knowledge of how to use energy forces could lead to the most absurd practices. Instead of striving for an animal's wellbeing by increasingly helping it to live in harmony with its archetypal energies, such knowledge could just be used, without conscience, for profitable ends. Similar tricks could be used in viticulture, but are quite at odds with an overall context of care for the natural world. For instance, it is possible to imprint water with energy information: adding 2 or 3 drops of such water will immediately improve the quality and taste of wine. But this is a kind of deception, for it is a later intervention rather than an integral part of the whole process. The effect will not be lasting and will be reversed at a later stage. So you can see that working with energies in this way could, alas, have an important economic potential. Instead, biodynamics aims to reinforce a connection that exists already rather than creating one arbitrarily.

Let us return to specific practice, though, and ask what actions are necessary to enhance planetary and stellar influences on a vineyard.

Quite simply, when a situation is propitious for the vine we will try to reinforce its influence. What do I mean by a favourable situation? There are three zodiac constellations which give heat impulses, and thus fruiting forces which the vine uses to form the grape. These constellations are: Ram, Lion and Archer.* We will not enter here into the specific quality of each of these influences. Those interested in these matters can read the excellent book by Fritz Julius referred to in the Bibliography, or the numerous books by Maria Thun. But to cut a long story short it is good, whenever possible, to enhance the vine's connection with these three influences, so as to develop the wine's full complexity. This is called 'trigon treatment'. Of course everyone is free to disagree with such an approach. Let us remember, though, that we are using astronomy, not astrology here — i.e. the actual position of the constellations, which differs by almost 30 degrees from that of astrology. We have to go back over 2,000 years to find a situation where astrological positions coincided with reality (although this does not mean that the latter no longer have any effect on the human being today, as we have passed through a long evolution whose memory is stored in our bodies. There is continual interaction between the past, the brief, beautiful present and the future).

Apart from these constellations there are two other heat or warmth — and thus fruiting — influences, this time via the planets Mercury and Saturn. The first has a shorter year than ours, and the other a year that is much longer (30 years).

---

* The English names are used, rather than the Latin, to highlight the fact that the astronomical reality is referred to, rather than astrological tradition (see further comment in text below).

Their effects are likewise very different. Mercury affects movement, sap circulation, growth, physical accumulation, and helps avert hindrances or illnesses. Saturn, by contrast, plays an important role in taste, maturity and concentration. The quality one admires in a wine is derived from Jupiter or Saturn. The book by Kranich (see Bibliography) offers many details. We would not have juicy and tasty fruits without these two influences. Jupiter helps juice formation in a fruit, while Saturn creates a concentration of taste. The key question for the viticulturist is how and at what moment to enhance them. It requires fine sensitivity to decide the right moment to harvest the grapes. By waiting for the grapes to start shrinking and concentrating you lose a great deal of juice (decreasing yield) but the taste shifts from fruity to a kind of mineral taste. At the same time the colour changes from a light, yellowish-green to a deep yellow, sometimes almost orange, giving rise to the depth and essential quality of an AOC.

Let's take an example: when a warmth planet, either Mercury or Saturn, is situated in front of a heat constellation, their combined effects are enhanced and enriched by this synergy. And apart from this, when the position of one or both of these planets in relation to the earth is, for example, 60° or 180° – the latter being called an opposition – the earth which is at the centre of this straight line linking the two planets receives their influences in an enhanced way.

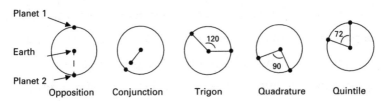

Different angles of positive (180°, 60°) or negative conjunctions (quadrature, quintile) of two planets with the earth. (From Maria Thun's Planting Calendar.)

There are other beneficial situations, but this must suffice as once instance of many. By tuning into and taking advantage of such effects, a biodynamic vineyard will benefit from them. What is also interesting here is that we can *enhance our vines' capacity to receive these influences,* for example by working the soil or dynamisation. Even light hoeing of the ground — that is, opening the skin of the soil — on a favourable date will render the micro-organisms more sensitive to these cosmic influences. It is like opening the shutters in a room to get a better idea of the weather outside. We can also choose such a date for dynamising a preparation. The vortex created in this process will thus imbue the substance to a greater extent with the specific, prevailing situation on that day, and then this information will be passed to the leaves or the soil. The vine, which has something of a nerve's sensitivity, is very receptive to these effects. But again, this is only one aspect of biodynamics, which is primarily effective through systematic application of its preparations once or twice each year. We can therefore practise it without any knowledge of the solar system. However the choice of date, also of course taking weather conditions into account, is an important complementary aspect. All these things have specific, measurable effects on yield, resistance to disease, storage quality, taste and aroma, and lead to very significant differences. Ultimately we are just helping the plant to express itself better. This is parallel, in the field of music, to improving the acoustics of a room, or the sound qualities of an instrument.

When we try to understand the profoundly original nature of each planet and each constellation, we acquire the possibility of creatively affecting the behaviour of our vines. Thus we can help them imbue themselves better with one or another influence which seems to us the right one for our vineyard. For example, we can understand that, when the sun is in the constellation of Archer in the depths of winter – thus at a time when nothing much emerges from the earth – the prevailing centripetal effects are very different from those of the Ram, which carries the strong centrifugal impulses of spring.

Let us also remember the moon which, in orbiting the earth, passes through the zodiac in 28 days, enabling us to use each of these specific forces during at least part of each month.

Plate 17 shows the importance of dates for harvesting and planting. The top picture is of identical vines, cut and planted in the same soil at an interval of several days. Some grow strongly while others fail to root. The bottom picture shows lettuces planted on either light (blossom) or water (leaf) days, at an interval of several days. The blossom day produces lettuces that tend to 'shoot' into flower. (Source: Maria Thun, *Sowing and Planting Calendar*)

This approach represents a return to a more artistic understanding of agriculture. Each day we can affect plant growth by means of our human qualities, and through simple, small actions based on our knowledge of the solar and stellar systems and the life they engender.

All this, as we have seen, is enhanced by the physical nature of a landscape, the choice of appropriate and well-raised vine varieties, specific animals adapted to the location, and many other factors which all act as receiver antennae for these impulses of life. We can regard all these factors as the musical notes which form a complete work. The more harmonious chords there are, the more vital and vibrant our wines will be. Resistance to oxidation in biodynamic wines, that is to destructive forces of ageing, is already a real demonstration of these facts.

This quick summary of biodynamic viticulture has the sole aim of showing wine lovers that it is not some superstitious sorcery based on an illusory view of the world, nor a wily communication ploy, but rather a reality which each of us comes to in our own way, in our own good time, to the extent we penetrate it with our understanding. Over time this agricultural approach, involving a greater discovery of the laws of life rather than those of matter alone, will increasingly gain ground. This is really the only way of offering consumers a healthy product, whose distinctive tastes are imbued with the landscape where it grows. Such produce is free from the artificial palate-flattery which we all too often think derives from the earth. If such artificial taste enhancement remains legally acceptable, at the risk of destroying the great concept of the AOC, at least this should be noted on the label so as to give consumers an opportunity to know whether what they are buying is an authentic taste of *terroir*. Isn't that the least of their rights?

6

Conclusion

When you drink a real wine, when you are transported by particular tastes or aromas, it is really a far-off, ethereal world that you are admiring, one distant from earthly laws. Each biodynamic agricultural act respects and sustains this other reality, transforming it into a physical quality which thereby becomes perceptible to our senses. By extending our knowledge, by giving back to the earth all its faculties through a respectful and artistic agriculture, the human being can come to play his full role. Then we will be able to receive, in return, more creative impulses from this world of resonance, whose nourishment we draw on unconsciously every day. The viticulturist would say: 'You are what you drink', and the farmer: 'You are what you eat.' This is a way to understand the legend of Dionysus, torn to pieces by the Titans on the orders of Hera, thus incarnating his forces of human individuality and compelling our descent to earth, where individuality can unfold. The Titans break the energy totality by ripping apart the body of Dionysus, thus making human beings enter time, the forces of Chronos, and leave Uranus, his father, the symbol of a unified whole.

Or, if you prefer, we have left the macrocosm and submerged ourselves in the fragmented microcosm. This separation created some dramas of course, and many partial and therefore incomplete and dangerous discoveries. In thinking ourselves masters of the world, we have brought this world close to the edge of destruction. But the legend of Dionysus is full of optimism. It tells us that his heart is saved by the goddess Pallas Athena, and entrusted to Zeus. A love affair brews which leads to the union of a 'mortal', Semele, with Zeus. From these new forces Dionysus is reborn, and subsequently takes on the role of teacher of agriculture, and the science and cultivation of the vine. This image shows us the rebirth of the human being through his heart forces, and through accessing a macrocosmic knowledge which we can put to good use. Biodynamics is Steiner's contribution to this rebirth, of which the younger generation is in such urgent and desperate need if it is to find its way back to a meaningful, sane and health-giving relationship with both earthly and ethereal realities.

Appendix

1. The 'Return to Terroir' Association

This group, created in France in 2001, now comprises 120 wine-growers from 12 different countries. Its purpose is to guarantee the full validity and expression of the 'appellations', and ensure wines of high quality and great originality.

To achieve this we act at three levels:

1. A legal guarantee of good agricultural practices. This means organic and/or biodynamic certification for the whole vineyard, for at least the past three years. The wine bearing this label comes from a vital soil that has not been treated with chemicals. The consumer thus has a legal assurance of quality. Ninety percent of group members practise biodynamic agriculture.

2. A guarantee that no actions undertaken in the cellar change the full expression of the AOC's taste. Proper agricultural practice means the cellar can be a birth or fruition procedure rather than a factory. All 300 aromatic yeast are banned, as is osmosis, GM, mechanical harvest (see quality charter). The winegrower signs a commitment to cellar procedures covering the past 3 years.

3. Wines are tasted by a committee consisting of the following well-known winegrowers:

Alsace: Olivier Umbrecht

Bourgogne: Anne Claude Leflaive and Pierre Morey

Champagne: David Leclapart

Rhone: Philippe de Blicquy

South: Raymond de Villeneuve

Loire: Nicolas Joly.

New members can only join the group by the committee's unanimous decision.

Three to four tastings are organized worldwide every year, and the costs of this are shared by all group members.

You can find more information at our website (in construction): www.biodynamy.com

2. The Charter of Quality

The system of evaluation outlined below does not speak in terms of 'biodynamic' or 'non-biodynamic', but simply of actions which permit an appellation to express itself fully. Thus one can go from one to three green stars, adding to this the usual notations used by wine guides. This system encourages winegrowers to aim for the highest standards, and informs consumers of the effects of measures, undertaken in the vineyards or in the cellar, on the appellation's expression.

One star:

Wine from a controlled appellation of origin has a particular taste linked to the type of soil and climate. Agriculture should therefore enhance the organic life of the soil and avoid all synthetic chemical products.

- No weed-killers/herbicides
- No chemical fertilisers
- No synthetic chemical products
- No systemic treatments
- No aromatic yeasts

Two stars:

In recent years the formidable advance of technology has enabled winegrowers to re-create the tastes that an inadequate agriculture had drained from grapes. A return to good practices renders this technology pointless, restoring the original taste to each wine without misleading the consumer.

- No mechanical harvesting
- No extraneous yeast that is foreign to the location
- No treating of the must with enzymes
- No concentrator that works by inverted osmosis
- No cryo-extraction
- No cold treatment that reaches freezing point

Three stars:
- No de-acidifying or re-acidifying
- No addition of ascorbic acid, nor of potassium sorbate
- No chaptalization, including concentrated must
- No irrigation

All winegrowers who adopt this charter will have authentic and thus inimitable wine since the relationship between soil and climate has a different 'countenance' in each location. Viticulturists who sign the charter in the presence of a notary public commit themselves to respecting this code of ethics in relation to the entire production cycle. Inspections can be carried out at any time by a member of the group.

Bibliography and Further Reading

Adams, G. and Whicher, O., *The Plant Between Sun and Earth*, London 1980

Bott, V., *An Introduction to Anthroposophic Medicine*, Sussex 2004

Cloos, W., *The Living Earth*, Cornwall 1977

Cook, W.E., *The Biodynamic Food and Cookbook*, Sussex 2006

Cook, W.E., *Foodwise*, Sussex 2003

Edwards, L., *The Vortex of Life*, Edinburgh 1993

Grohmann, G., *The Plant, A Guide to Understanding Its Nature*, London 1974

Hauschka, R., *The Nature of Substance*, London 1983

Julius, Frits H., *The Imagery of the Zodiac*, Edinburgh 1993

Kolisko, Drs. E. and L., *Agriculture of Tomorrow*, Bournemouth 1978

Pelikan, W., *Healing Plants*, New York 1997

Podolinsky, A., *Biodynamic Agriculture, Introductory Lectures*, vols. I and II, 1985

Pfeiffer, E., *Sensitive Crystallization Process*, New York 1975

Schwenk, T., *Sensitive Chaos*, London 1965

Soper, J., *Studying the 'Agriculture Course'*, West Midlands 1976

Steiner, R., *Agriculture Course*, Sussex 2004

Steiner, R., *The Spiritual Hierarchies*, New York 1996

Thun, M., *The Biodynamic Sowing and Planting Calendar*, Edinburgh 2006 (and yearly publication)

Thun, M., *The Biodynamic Year*, Sussex 2007

Thun, M., *Gardening for Life,* Stroud 2000

Thun, M., *Results from the Biodynamic Sowing and Planting Calendar*, Edinburgh 2004

Contacts

Nicolas Joly – Clos de la Coulée de serrant – Château de la Roche
aux Moines – 49170 Savennières – France
Tel: 0033 (0)2 41 72 22 32 – Fax: 0033 (0)2 41 72 28 68
e-mail: coulee-de-serrant@wanadoo.fr
website: www.coulee-de-serrant.com

See the Demeter website for links to biodynamic organizations
around the world: www.demeter.net   info@demeter.net

UNITED KINGDOM:
Biodynamic Agricultural Association
The Painswick Inn Project
Gloucester Street
Stroud
Glos. GL5 1QG
Tel./Fax: 01453 759501
e-mail: office@biodynamic.org.uk
www.biodynamic.org.uk

USA:

Biodynamic Farming and Gardening Association, Inc.

25844 Butler Road

Junction City

OR 97448

Tel.: 888 516-7797 or 541 998-0105

Fax: 541 998-0106

e-mail: biodynamic@aol.com

www.biodynamics.com

Picture Credits

All photos and illustrations by Nicolas Joly except for Plate 2 by Kate Mount, Plate 8 by Bernard Morales (courtesy Nicolas Joly), Plates 12 & 13 by Bernard Prieur and M. F. Tesson, Association Presence (courtesy Nicolas Joly), Plate 15 by Christian Marcel (courtesy Nicolas Joly), and Plate 17 by Maria Thun.

Also available from Clairview:

The Biodynamic Food and Cookbook
Real Nutrition That Doesn't Cost the Earth
Wendy E. Cook

'In my experience, biodynamic food is of exceptional quality and taste — so I use it when I can. And it's good for my health!' — Antony Worrall Thompson

'I know from my own experience that eating biodynamically grown food ... leaves a fine and lasting impression on the palate.' — Patrick Holden, Director, Soil Association

Biodynamics is about respect for nature, sustainability and spiritual ecology — but most of all it is about flavoursome, nutritious and enjoyable food! This is a book rich in information, beautifully illustrated and packed with healthy yet tasty recipes.

It is a movement that is supported by top chefs, expert viniculturists and numerous celebrities. Even Prince Charles has introduced its methods at his Gloucestershire farm. Yet biodynamic agriculture had humble beginnings. In 1924 a small group gathered to hear the philosopher and scientist Rudolf Steiner give a series of lectures. At a time when industrial farming and mass production were on the rise, Steiner spoke of the qualitative aspects of food, and outlined an agricultural method founded on a holistic perception of nature.

Illustrated with hundreds of full-colour photographs, *The Biodynamic Food and Cookbook* explains the principles behind biodynamics, and places it in the context of food and cooking throughout the ages. Wendy Cook takes us on a journey through the four seasons, presenting over 150 delicious recipes based on many years of working with biodynamic nutrition. She studies the ethics of food, the foundations of a balanced diet, and conjures up the colour and vibrancy of Mallorca, which has contributed so much to her personal approach. There are supplementary sections on breads, sauces, salads, desserts, drinks and much more.

256pp; 30 × 21 cm; £18.99; ISBN: 978 1 905570 01 0